Life Along the
San Andreas Fault

By the Same Author

VASECTOMY: *The Truth and Consequences*
of the Newest Form of Birth Control—Male Sterilization

Life Along the
San Andreas Fault

JOHN J. FRIED

Saturday Review Press

NEW YORK

Published simultaneously in Canada by
Doubleday Canada Ltd., Toronto.

Library of Congress Catalog Card Number: 72–88649

ISBN 0–8415–0233–1

Saturday Review Press
380 Madison Avenue
New York, New York 10017

PRINTED IN THE UNITED STATES OF AMERICA

Design by Tere LoPrete

Contents

List of Illustrations

Between pages 180 and 181

All photographs courtesy of the U.S. Geological Survey

Acknowledgments

A great many people gave unstintingly of their expertise to help me with this book. Many took time to talk extensively about California's earthquake problems, to guide me through voluminous professional and academic literature, to read the manuscript, checking its accuracy. I am particularly indebted to David Leeds of Dames and Moore; Dr. Robert Wallace, Don Nichols, Dr. C. B. Raleigh, and Dr. G. Brent Dalrymple of the United States Geological Survey; Dr. Robert Nason of the Earthquake Mechanism Laboratory, U.S. Department of Commerce; Dr. Edward Stainbrook of the Department of Human Behavior, the University of Southern California; Sal Bianco of the Diridon Research Corporation, consultant to the California legislature's Joint Committee on Seismic Safety; Professor C. Martin Duke, Professor of Engineering, UCLA; Dr. Samuel Aroni of the UCLA School of Architecture and Urban Planning; Mrs. Charlotte Guerrant of the Department of Civil Engineering, California Institute of Technology; the Caltech News Bureau; Mr. Ed O'Connor, director of Building and Safety, Long Beach; and Robert Shaman of Dames and Moore.

Two people in particular are closely responsible for this book: Charles Sopkin of Saturday Review Press, who suggested that an in-depth look at life along the San Andreas Fault might be worthwhile, and my wife, Chris, whose editing cleared some of the early fog and whose speedy typing helped clear the deadline.

From the Scourge of the Earthquake,
O Lord, Deliver Us.
Roman Catholic litany

If a Builder Build a House for a Man
and Do Not Make its Construction
Firm, and the House which he has Built
Collapses and Causes the Death of the
Owner of the House, that Builder Should
Be Put to Death.

Code of Hammurabi
(c. 1955–1913 B. C.)

Introduction

In the early dawn of April 18, 1906, an intense shaking, accompanied by the roar of buildings crumbling into dust, swept across northern California. In city after city, men, women, and children in nightclothes rushed from their homes, startled by the shaking, terrified by the din of wooden beams, walls, and frames groaning and croaking under strain, of furniture crashing against walls, of glassware, silverware, pots, and pans crashing from cabinets and cupboards.

In the sixty seconds that marked the great earthquake along the San Andreas Fault, hundreds were killed: 112 in the rubble that once had been the Agnews State Insane Asylum near San Jose, 100 at one rooming house in San Francisco, 125 at another, scores at still a third. And, though the earthquake had spent its own furies in less than a minute, it unleashed forces of destruction that were to last for days. Overturned stoves, bared electrical wiring, broken chimneys spawned fires that swept through Santa Rosa and San

Francisco. Virtually surrounded by water, San Franciscans could only watch helplessly as their city burned. Major water mains crossing the San Andreas on their way into the city had been destroyed by the earthquake. Pumping stations that might have drawn water from the ocean had been reduced to piles of brick by the tremor. Able-bodied men—residents, visitors to the city, sightseers who had flocked to San Francisco from unaffected areas—were pressed, often at gunpoint by soldiers, into service to beat down the flames in any way possible. The worn-out fire department, hoping to clear zones the fire could not breach, tried to use dynamite and gunpowder to clear away wooden houses and commercial buildings. More often than not the resulting blasts themselves started fires or spread burning cinders to still untouched buildings. In one neighborhood, the Latin Quarter, an Italian restaurant turned its huge reservoir of red wine over to fire fighters who used it to save three hundred homes around the restaurant.

With the flames clearly winning, San Franciscans abandoned their homes. A few, able to afford the one-hundred-dollar fares some boat owners were demanding for transportation out of the burning city, found their way across the Bay to Oakland, which had been spared fire. Most stayed in the city, finding refuge where possible, pushing, pulling, or carrying what few possessions they had been able to salvage. "Even the smallest child carried something, or pushed it before him on a rocking chair, or dragged it behind him in a trunk, and the thing he carried was the index of the refugee's strongest bent," Mary Austin, a San Francisco author, wrote. "All the women saved their best hats and their babies, and, if there were no babies, some of them pushed pianos up the cement pavements." By the time the exodus from the burning parts of the city had been completed, more than two hundred thousand persons were living in Golden Gate Park. (Other earthquakes have spawned fires, although refugees from burning areas have not always been lucky in finding a safe haven. In 1923, an intense series of earthquakes set off widespread fires in Tokyo. In one district, between twenty thousand and forty thousand persons crowded into an area they thought safe from the flames. But the widespread fires, combined with unusual weather conditions, set off fire storms that rushed through the supposedly safe area of Tokyo with up to 240-mile-an-hour winds. All of the refugees suffocated or burned to death.)

The massive displacement of people in San Francisco created its own havoc. Profiteers extorted exorbitant sums to help businessmen save their records. Anyone with a cart could command up to fifty dollars per carload of goods or records hauled to safety. Some grocers tripled and quadrupled their food prices. Looters roamed the city, sifting through wrecked and abandoned homes, stealing from corpses.

Harried and tired soldiers, as well as outraged volunteers and rescue workers, often took the law into their own hands when confronted by illegal activities. When soldiers found one grocer charging one dollar for each loaf of bread, they seized the store and passed out free food to those who needed it. When the owner of the store protested the action, the soldiers pushed him to the wall and executed him on the spot. "One afternoon in front of the Palace Hotel," two observers wrote, "a crowd of workers in the ruins discovered a miscreant in the act of robbing a corpse of its jewels. Without delay he was seized, a rope secured, and he was immediately strung up to a beam which was left standing in the ruined entrance. No sooner had he been hoisted up and a hitch taken in the rope than one of his fellow criminals was captured. . . . A knot was quickly tied and the wretch was soon adorning the hotel entrance by the side of the other dastard."

Near the northernmost boundary of the area devastated by the San Francisco earthquake, the little town of Jenner nestles into the hills overlooking the Pacific Ocean, not far from where the Russian River finally dumps its waters after turning and twisting its way out of the northern California hinterlands.

On foggy, misty days, when the steady rain is just a redundancy to the gloom, the town streets and roads are deserted. The five hundred or so townspeople stay within their hillside homes. The scores of young people who have dropped out of the civilizations of San Francisco, Los Angeles, and New York to settle in the area and set up their cottage industries—hand-made redwood planters; rough-hewn, turn-of-the-century model trains; leather goods; antiques—have little reason to pass through town. Two or three of the men might wander in for last-minute weekend provisions, stopping in the Jenner-by-the-Sea Restaurant to warm up before heading back into the woods. They know the restaurant has come to an amicable truce with their lifestyles and, absent-mindedly passing their fingers through hair and around chins, they move past the sign half-heartedly warning that only those with *combed* long hair and beards will be served and hurry into the side room where a roaring fireplace is radiating welcome heat. When they have been sufficiently heartened by the warmth, they make their way back to their backwoods homesteads, marked by only an occasional lighted window, a thin plume of smoke trailing from a random chimney, or a wet dog sleeping under a small portico.

Neither established townspeople nor newly arrived urban dropouts worry about the San Andreas Fault, lurking just off the Jenner coast, hidden beneath the misty, cold waters. Essentially unfelt since the 1906 shudder, it has become a geological Loch Ness monster, assuming a semimythical quality, nothing more than a possible half-truth, only a remote threat to life.

The same mystical aura surrounds the fault over much of its more-than-650-mile span. It seems to have little bearing on civilization, especially where its trace is a string of lakes or deep, lovely valleys whose surrounding hills are covered with lush vegetation and hidden by rolling, thick fogs; where it runs through groves of oranges and orchards of apples; where, stark and gray, it cuts through desolate semi-barren plains, diverting streams; even where, in the southernmost part of the state, it breaks and shatters into a jumble of subsidiary faults that bring the entire width of the state under its power.

There is, however, nothing mystical or romantic about the San Andreas, and experts, ranging from geophysicists to engineers, watch with horror tinged by fascination as California's spiraling urbanization plays a cat-and-mouse game with the San Andreas, its subsidiary faults, and with many of the dozens of other dangerous faults, small and large, active in California.

"Seventy-four million persons have died as a result of earthquakes," *Mosaic*, the magazine of the National Science Foundation estimates. "Just in the second quarter of this century, three hundred and fifty thousand have died. It would appear that the United States has been extraordinarily lucky so far. Less than twelve hundred have died in American earthquakes even though the United States has had several great earthquakes. The biggest occurred in the nineteenth century when the local population was dispersed, and great modern ones have taken place in as yet sparsely populated parts of the country. But it is clear that someday—perhaps soon—the relentlessly increasing population curve and the earthquake curve will cross."

In California, the stage for the confrontation has been a long time in the making. In 1857, when the Fort Tejon earthquake became the last great earthquake to release some of the forces contained within the San Andreas Fault in the area near Los Angeles, the southern basins and valleys were virtually uninhabited. When a powerful tremor on the San Andreas struck the central part of the state in 1838, it did little more than scare the wits out of a few assorted settlers. And even when the great earthquake of 1906 struck San Francisco, only a few hundred thousand persons were in the Bay Area. In the south, when the moderate earthquake of 1933 rippled out of the Newport-Inglewood Fault near the Long Beach area, a mere 2.5 million persons were scattered around the Los Angeles metropolitan area.

The picture, however, in both southern and northern California has changed drastically. More than 4 million persons already make their homes in the San Francisco area, and the population of the once lightly inhabited area will reach 7.5 million by 1990. Today, almost 11 million persons live crowded in and around Los Angeles, and within a few years, the number will reach 20 million. In fact, by the year 2000, the Urban Land Institute estimates, almost one out of every fifteen persons in the United States will live in the megalopolis stretching from south of Los Angeles to just north of San Francisco, the very coastal area that is the most prone to earthquakes.

California's earliest settlers—the religious pioneers who established twenty-one missions from the southern to the northern part of the state, the gold prospectors who came pell-mell in the nineteenth century to make their fortunes, and the adventuresome men and women who came in the early twentieth century—did from time to time build their homes, their businesses, their shacks astride active faults or on the unstable soils that are also prone to fail under earthquake forces. But by and large, with plenty of land to spare, they were able to build where they found, by accident or design, good ground to support their shelters. "The sites of the cities were not selected with the idea that they would grow to present sizes," Dr. John S. Steinhart, formerly of the Office of Science and Technology in the Executive Office of the President, explains. "The good land, the easy land to build on, and the convenient land went first, and the pressures grow ever more intense as the urban areas sprawl out larger and larger and press into service those areas filled in from the sea, former swamps and steep hillsides—those areas which were bypassed by the original construction and original expansion because they were very difficult. The issue is one that presses us very hard."

The issue presses even harder as people continue to pour into the state in search of its good weather, its easy living, and its promise of a new start in life, as those already in California spread to the countryside, seeking relief from the cities. "It is very hard to counter the economic development forces when they are as tough as they are in California," a professor of economics at the University of California at Los Angeles (UCLA) mentioned in an interview. "People could be sold a home at the end of a runway if they are shown the house at the right time. In the case of earthquake-prone land, you have a kind of flood-plain mentality involved, except that it seems even more perverse." The result, then, is that as the economic and population pressures grow, fault-scarred land is snapped up almost as fast as it is offered. Unstable land away from the fault areas of the state is bought, developed, and sold, often without the first thought being given to its susceptibility to earthquake forces.

The California State Division of Real Estate has estimated, for example, that as many as fifty new subdivisions are thrown up every year across known earthquake fault zones. Villages, towns, cities, office buildings, single-family homes, multistoried apartment complexes, intricate highway interchanges, power stations, dams, have been, and are, erected although no one has looked for earthquake faults (or has analyzed the stability of soils) beneath their foundations. The Hayward fault zone, a major San Andreas branch, seems particularly blessed with man's construction efforts, despite the fault's great propensity for classical seismic activity: tiny creeps of several millimeters a year that can slowly tear a building apart over several years, or sudden thrusts of the ground that can move the earth forward several feet during a fair-sized earthquake, destroying a building in one fell swoop.

The most vital of installations are not exempt from the fault-zone area. In one city, a telephone building with vital underground trunk lines sits squarely atop the fault. The Alameda County Civil Defense Operations Center was blindly constructed over the fault zone. Schools and hospitals dot the area. According to a study released by the National Center for Earthquake Research in Menlo Park, California, several Richmond Unified School District buildings, some completed within only the last five or six years, were built over the fault, as were some structures of the Contra Costa Junior College campus in San Pablo. According to official surveys, there are as many as fifty schools and hospitals on sites subject to severe earthquake damage through fault action. "This relation of school to active strand is so common," says George Gates, formerly an assistant chief geologist for the U.S. Geological Survey (USGS) and now an advisor to it and to the state of California, "you can . . . draw a line from school to school and you've pretty well outlined the Hayward fault zone." Adds Lloyd Cluff, vice-president of an Oakland firm of consulting geologists and engineers and an advisor to the California legislature's Joint Committee on Seismic Safety, "The way many hospitals and schools were built around here, you'd think they used the fault as a guide for where to place those buildings. There are hospitals on the Hayward Fault that are thirteen and fourteen stories high and are prime candidates for destruction if the fault moves. They should be abandoned, but some of them are only five years old and represent multimillion-dollar investments."

The vast majority of California homeowners choose to disregard earthquake problems when they purchase land or homes. "We are not worrisome people," Mrs. Hans Levenberger, whose home in Portola Highlands, a San Francisco suburb, sits in the midst of the San Andreas fault zone, says. "You can look into the fault from the upstairs window. But then, if you worry, you don't live anyplace. We just wanted a place where we could live and which we could afford. After looking at a hundred houses, you don't worry about earthquakes anymore."

While the disregard for safety seems flippant, neither the layman who buys a house (or rents an apartment) in a hazardous area nor the developer who puts the home or the apartment building on marginal land can be held solely responsible for increasing California's earthquake risks. Where public officials are not tripping over each other to accommodate private real estate interests pressing to bring more and more suburbs to unsafe land, they are often involving their cities and towns in expansion schemes to add taxable acreage to the city rolls. In the process, they themselves open development of hazardous land, ignoring the fact that potential disaster on the new land may diminish property values and lower tax revenues, or that repeated damage to city services extended to the new land may cost the city sizable amounts of money in repair and maintenance.

Public officials in cities where seismic activity has been taking its toll in older, developed neighborhoods also close their eyes to earthquake problems. They order the removal

of older buildings damaged by seismic activity in hazardous
land and then move to use the same hazard-filled area, often
on a more intense and grandiose level.

One man, for example, had acquired—by making default
payments—some choice property two blocks from Hayward's city hall, a structure that is slowly being torn apart
by the Hayward Fault, which, as it runs through the city's
midsection, passes squarely beneath the building, tearing at
its foundations. "The property has a great view of the Bay
Area and he had grand visions of putting up high-rise apartment buildings all over the site," Lloyd Cluff says with
barely concealed amusement. "He came in to see us for recommendations and I told him, because I knew the Hayward
Fault was there, that even without going out to the site to
do an inspection I could tell him to forget it. I told him he
could find engineering geologists who would give the site a
clean bill of health and that he could probably go ahead
with his plans. But I told him he'd be stupid to do so and
that he could even be held criminally liable if the buildings
collapsed in an earthquake. He just slumped in his chair.

"But he decided he wanted us to go ahead with a study
anyway to see what we could suggest. We wiped out 60 to
70 percent of the land as too hazardous for construction, although we did find a piece of land where we told him he
could put up some homes and be safe. His planners were
ready to kill us. Well, after two or three months they cooled
off and came back wanting to know if they could put in a
McDonald's or pizza parlors. Of course, aesthetically, that
was another matter, but I told him that, as long as they were
built right, they could go ahead."

But when the developer submitted his new plans to the
city of Hayward, Cluff adds, it became evident that the city
government cared little about the city's uneasy relationship
with the Hayward Fault as it runs through the middle of the
downtown area, and that the city's various departments—

building, planning, and zoning—had done little to pursue a responsible plan for using the land in the city according to the seismic risks presented. "When we met with the departments and attended hearings on the project," Cluff says, "the zoning people started accusing us of writing a slanted report just to help the man put in a McDonald's! One councilman said he didn't even know there was a fault running through Hayward. Anyway, all the recommendations were turned down.

"Before our client got the property, the city, faced with an urban renewal project, had gone out and hired an architectural firm with a national reputation to advise them on making the city more attractive. The firm, without the benefit of geological advice, suggested the high-rise buildings for the downtown area. That's what the city wanted and that's what they were determined to get. They are already tearing down buildings in the city that were damaged by the Hayward Fault, and they are putting up other structures right over the same spots."

Hazardous land alone would not kill or injure people. Anyone standing directly on a fault or on loose, sandy soil during an earthquake might be thrown off his feet by the vigorous shaking (The tales of men and women being devoured by opening and closing fissures during an earthquake are more fancy than fact. After the 1906 San Francisco earthquake, people talked in hushed tones of a fissure that had reputedly opened to swallow a cow and had then closed swiftly, leaving only the unfortunate animal's tail protruding from the earth as evidence of the tremor's cannibalism. The real story, unearthed later by investigators, proved to be less dramatic. In the earthquake's aftermath, the frightened animal had apparently stumbled into the fissure, dying in the process. Would-be rescuers, finding the animal beyond help, chose to bury it where it had come to rest.), but he would suffer nothing more than slightly ruffled dignity as he toppled, feet in the air. Land is made treacherous by construction, and while a few highly qualified engineers strive to design the best buildings they can, improperly used land, unfortunately, is all too often covered with badly designed and badly executed construction. In many earthquakes, it will be the combination of bad land and bad buildings that will set the trap for millions of Californians.

Some live and work in buildings erected before the minimal building codes now in use were adopted to regulate construction. The designs of many of these buildings, some dating back to the turn of the century, were, and are, often inadequate. The construction methods and the materials used left, and leave, a great deal to be desired. "In California mortar has often been so bad that after several destructive earthquakes it has been profitable to collect bricks from damaged buildings, wash off the remains of the mortar with a hose, and sell secondhand bricks practically as good as new," Dr. Charles Richter wrote in his book *Elementary Seismology* in 1958. "At present, even when good mortar is used, it is commonly applied so rapidly that the full bonding effect is not reached."

Furthermore, over the last ten or fifteen years, engineers and public officials have been given notice that the most modern of building codes—the theoretical legal protectors of life and property—are barely up to the task of protecting those who live in seismic areas like California. Earthquakes in Mexico City, Caracas, Chile, Anchorage, and Santa Rosa have warned time and time again that even the newer buildings are potential death weapons in an earthquake and that many engineers who build merely according to code, as one activist in the engineering field has put it, are designing "earthquake hazards waiting to happen."

As far as many earthquake experts are concerned, the interplay between bad land and bad construction (not to mention bad land, bad construction, and inadequate disaster relief preparation) will come to climax in an all-too-probable great earthquake somewhere along the San Andreas Fault. Almost every reputable earthquake researcher is convinced that a tremor of sizable proportions along the San Andreas is already long overdue. Sober scientists at the U.S. Geological Survey have put the chances at seven out of ten that a great San Andreas earthquake—measuring 8 or more on the Richter scale—will strike in the next thirty years.

Any number of earthquake and disaster experts—including Dr. Charles Richter and Dr. Clarence Allen, both of the California Institute of Technology (Caltech), Karl Steinbrugge, a leading structural engineer and crusader for earthquake safety, the California legislature's Joint Committee on Seismic Safety, and the directors of public-safety commissions and bureaus in several counties and cities—have repeatedly sketched out the results of a great earthquake along the fault. If the tremor is an encore of the 1906 event, striking the northern part of the state, they foresee 350,000 casualties, including 3500 deaths, within the San Francisco city and county limits alone. According to C. Martin Duke, Professor of Engineering at the University of California at Los Angeles, if an 8-pointer were to strike near the Antelope Valley town of Pearblossom, about thirty-five miles from downtown Los Angeles, the damage would be devastating over nearly twelve hundred square miles of intensely developed land. Trees would snap in half, chimneys would be hurled from and through rooftops, homes would somersault down hillsides, apartment buildings would collapse in a heap of dust, railroad tracks would snap and bend, cement sidewalks and freeway overpasses would crumble. The property damage alone could exceed forty-eight billion dollars. At least three thousand persons would be killed under *favorable* circumstances. Given the right time of day—if the earthquake were to strike at nine in the morning, when freeways would be clogged, elevators full, when thousands of persons would be on the sidewalks under the shadow of old buildings, when office buildings and schools would be filling—the death toll could soar. "It is distressingly easy to visualize ten thousand deaths," Duke says.

The sudden shudder along the San Andreas is not the only possibility. The San Andreas's subsidiary faults—the Hayward in the northern part of the state and the Imperial and the San Jacinto faults in the southern part—are capable of triggering a powerful earthquake, as are any of the major and minor faults that are not part of the San Andreas fault zone. Duke estimates, for example, that if a 7.2 earthquake were to strike along the Newport-Inglewood Fault—one that was discovered in 1920 and which was responsible for the 1933 Long Beach earthquake—near an intersection in south-central Los Angeles, close to three thousand persons could be killed and more than forty billion dollars' worth of property could be destroyed or damaged.

On February 9, 1971, Californians were given a preview of what, in the coming years of intensifying urbanization and increased construction, may be the greatest seismic danger to their safety and property: the small, moderate earthquake that, originating on any fault, large or small, can be expected with far greater regularity and at shorter intervals than the large, dramatic earthquake.

The February 9 tremor struck the northern tip of the Los Angeles metropolitan area, a section of the San Fernando Valley where 95 percent of the buildings and public projects have been constructed since 1933, including many erected within the last decade. Destruction wrought by the relatively moderate earthquake—6.4 on the Richter scale—totaled more than half a billion dollars and killed 64 persons. More than 800 homes, 65 apartment buildings, and 574 commercial buildings were severely damaged or completely destroyed. More than 5000 homes, 265 apartment buildings, and more than 1000 commercial buildings, though not totally destroyed, suffered appreciable damage. Almost 30,000 other buildings suffered lesser damage.

Olive View Hospital, a twenty-seven-million-dollar facility, finished less than a year before the earthquake, was damaged beyond repair by the tremor. Of the more than six hundred persons in the building at the time, patients and members of a skeletal crew (the earthquake struck at one minute before six in the morning), only two persons died of injuries, and only two patients died when the electricity failed, shutting off their respirators. The death toll, however, might have been worse because, as a California Institute of Technology study of the tremor reported, "it is doubtful if the already badly damaged columns [supporting the building] could have stood up for another five seconds of strong ground shaking."

Even if the columns had stood, patients and staff would have been in dire danger had fire broken out in the hospital. At the end of each of the hospital's four wings, a fire escape tower had been built. However, during the earthquake, three of the four towers completely collapsed and the fourth one detached itself and leaned away. "Patients attempting to escape through the corridors," Dr. Samuel Aroni of the UCLA School of Architecture and Urban Planning says, "had a good view of the collapsed towers." Although no fire did break out, it took fire departments almost eight hours to evacuate all the patients from the damaged building.

It was, in fact, an irony lost on almost no one that the most dangerous place to have been during the earthquake was a hospital. In addition to Olive View, other medical facilities (some of which were also relatively new) were also destroyed or severely damaged, including Paicoma Lutheran Hospital, Indian Hills Medical Center, Kaiser Memorial Hospital, and Holy Cross Hospital.

The earthqake, however, left no sector without its toll. A $45-million water-treatment plant, still under construction,

suffered between $5 and $6 million worth of damage. A
$110-million converter station, completed in 1970, suffered
$30 million in damage. A San Fernando juvenile-detention
facility, also completed shortly before the earthquake, at a
cost of $6.5 million, was damaged beyond repair.

Similar earthquakes have always struck California, and
have struck it with some regularity. But as long as the population was dispersed, the danger from the small, frequent
quakes, though real, was held to a minimum. Now, as the
population grows, as it spreads out in hazardous construction over marginal land, many of the small earthquakes, remote and unfelt because they struck at a distance
from urban areas, will extend their power, chipping away at
property, chipping away at lives, until, when some final tally
is taken, they may very well have claimed as many lives as
and inflicted more suffering than the great earthquake that
lurks somewhere in the San Andreas Fault.

To help us understand why earthquakes will continue to
threaten man, why they may kill or maim three thousand
persons in one shudder, three thousand people in thirty different earthquakes, or tens of thousands of men, women,
and children in a combination of small and large earthquakes, the discussion that follows has been divided into
three parts. First, in Chapters One and Two, we focus on
the land beneath our feet. Generally, what do scientists
know about earthquakes? Specifically, what do they know
about the San Andreas Fault and other dangerous faults in
California? With this geological background, we examine, in
Chapters Three through Seven, how the land is made
treacherous to those who live upon it. What roles do politics
and pressures from private-interest groups play in bringing
those areas most susceptible to earthquake forces into use
for construction? How are building codes written and what
measures do they require for protection against earthquake
damage? Why are these codes inadequate? Finally, in Chap-

ters Eight through Ten, we investigate the people who live in earthquake-riddled land. How are they psychologically affected by earthquakes? What is and is not being done to help those whose lives are disrupted by tremors? What needs to be done if California is to be made, if not completely earthquake-resistant, then at least earthquake-safe?

PART I

The Land Beneath Our Feet

Chapter One

Throughout time, nature has generously dispensed tornadoes, hurricanes, cyclones, and floods to destroy mankind's
homes, to sweep away his grain and livestock, to kill and
maim men, women, and their children. Yet, for all the harm
inflicted by these freaks of nature, only the earthquake—
that unannounced, sudden, and terrifying shudder of the
ground beneath his feet—has elicited in man a profound,
universal consciousness of terror. Unable to see or understand the causes of the ground tremors, men over the eons
spun elaborate, fanciful explanations. The glimmerings of
understanding would have to wait the coming of the nineteenth century, and astute scientific comprehension, the last
half of the twentieth century.

To the ancient Semitic tribes meandering through the
arid deserts or the then-lush valleys of the Middle East, the
shaking of the earth was a sure sign of the Lord's displeas-

ure. The tremors of one earthquake had hardly subsided before some anonymous Levite singer or musician found his way to quill and papyrus to scribble down the humble prayers of sinners in the hands of an angry God. "The mountains skipped like rams and little hills like lambs," the Levite wrote in Psalm 114. "Tremble thou earth, at the presence of the Lord, at the presence of the God of Jacob; which turned the rock into a standing water, the flint into a fountain of waters." Psalm 60, coming perhaps after another earthquake, is simpler and to the point: "Thou has broken it; heal the breaches thereof; for it shaketh."

In the Mediterranean, the Hebrews were not alone in experiencing earthquakes. The Greeks were shaken from their feet from time to time, and, when an earthquake struck, peasants and Spartan kings alike fell to their knees in devoted, fervent prayer to Poseidon, the god of the sea and the god of the earthquake. When they were not praying to Poseidon, hoping to stave off further earthquakes, the Greeks were littering the coastline of the Mediterranean with numerous sanctuaries in his honor.

Around the world, the ancient explanations for earthquakes were almost as diverse as the peoples experiencing the tremors. As far as the tribes of what is now Bulgaria were concerned, earthquakes struck when an enormous water buffalo, assigned to carry the earth upon his back, grew tired of the burden and shifted weight from one foot to another to ease his load. In several primitive lands it was thought that the earth was supported by a huge hog who periodically scratched himself against a tree, in the process setting off earthquakes. The Algonquins, a North American Indian tribe, believed that a huge tortoise bore the earth upon its shell, and that earthquakes struck when the earth jiggled on the giant reptile's back. Others ascribed the mighty task of supporting the earth to spiders, frogs, whales, and serpents, all of whom made movements that set off earthquakes. The Hindus on the sub-Asian continent believed that a serpent by the name of Hirani Ashshana had stolen the earth from its resting place on an expanse of water and had hidden it in the Seventh Heaven. However, Vishnu, the second personage of the Hindu Trinity, had succeeded in finding the earth and returning it to its liquid support. But the theft had changed the earth somehow, and when it was placed back upon the water, instead of floating happily as it had before the larceny, it began to sink and settle. Chagrined, Vishnu cast about for a way to keep the earth floating, finally hitting upon a solution embodying poetic justice and practicality. He ordered seven serpents to pay for their brother's grievous crime by taking turns in holding the earth above water. Unfortunately, every time one serpent reported for duty and slithered under the earth as another serpent slid off for a rest, the earth, as it was jiggled onto its new supporter, was wracked by earthquakes.

The gods-and-serpents theories suited the more superstitious ancients. More rational men, the Greek philosophers among them, strove to put some scientific, some logical explanation behind the destructive and violent movements beneath their feet. The philosopher Thales, for example, held the view that the world did float on water (though there was no room for reptiles or aquatic animals in his concept). This simple fact, he said, accounted for the new springs that often spurted forth during and after an earthquake. Anaxagoras, friend to Pericles, and a philosopher who preceded Christ by some five hundred years, proposed that earthquakes resulted when sections of the earth cracked and caved in. Anaxagoras even had a backup theory: earthquakes, he said, might be the aftermath of fires that raged through the inside of mountains, forcing their fragile crust to tremble, crack, and finally collapse. The succession of aftershocks that accompanied most earthquakes, Anaxagoras said, were brought on by huge rocks that, loosened from the inside walls of the mountains, bounced around inside the earth before they finally came to rest, somewhere deep in the terrestrial interior.

One of the more ingenious ideas—and one repeated well into the centuries following Christ—was proposed by Aristotle. Aristotle considered the earthquake phenomenon and ruminated about the often stifling and listless atmosphere reported to precede most earthquakes. For him, the two phenomena obviously were related. There were times, he said, when all the winds and breezes in a given area somehow had been forced into the earth's interior. There, they mixed with other trapped masses of air and gas and in combination with them raged through the earth's internal cavities, desperately seeking a way to gain their freedom. The tremendous forces rushing about, hurtling themselves against the restraining rocks, Aristotle said, set off earthquakes. Almost sixteen hundred years after Aristotle, Conrad of Megenburg seconded the philosopher, writing:

now earthquakes originate in this manner, that within subterranean cavities, and especially in the interior recesses of mountains, vapors are compacted together in such vast quantities, and under such tremendous pressure, as to exceed at times all means of restraining them. They crowd in all directions against the walls of the interior caverns, fly from one to the other of them, and continue to augment in volume until they have surcharged an entire mountain. The increase of these vapors is occasioned by the stars, especially Mars and Jupiter. When now the vapors are confined for a long time within the subterranean cavities, the pressure becomes so prodigious that they burst forth with enormous violence and rend mountains asunder. Even when they fail to break completely through the crust, they are yet able to produce a severe shock.

As commendable as the philosophical attempts were to give earthquakes a rational rhyme and reason, they did not come close to the truth. To explain accurately any natural phenomenon, scientists must be able to define its character- istics, to sort out and measure precisely its various compo- nents, and to outline accurately its effects. It was well into the nineteenth century before the first real attempts were made to define the nature of earthquakes.

The first crude efforts to come to a scientific understand- ing of earthquakes came with the development of charts, or indices, that allowed scientists to classify and compare earthquakes according to the damage they inflicted. One of the first attempts to develop a method of assessing and com- paring earthquakes was developed by an Irish engineer in the 1860s. The engineer, Robert Mallet, outlined four dif- ferent categories, or zones, of earthquake damage. Zone one included the area of greatest damage, a section where a whole town might have been destroyed by an earthquake. Zone two was reserved to outline an area where large build- ings had been destroyed or torn apart and people thrown to the ground. Zone three included areas where the earth- quake had wrought only minor damage, injuring or killing no one. The last and outermost zone drawn represented sites in which trembling had been felt but where the tremor had caused no damage.

Mallet's four-zone charting method was a start, but a crude one. The growing network of earth scientists around the world knew that earthquakes could cause damage much too diversified to be squeezed into merely four categories. If an Italian seismologist describing a Mediterranean earth quake to a colleague in Japan were to write him that the earthquake had been a category-two tremor on Mallet's chart, he would be telling him very little. The Japanese seismologist would know that large buildings had been de- stroyed or completely leveled. But what kind of buildings had they been? the Japanese would be left asking himself. Masonry? Wood? Had they been of recent or vintage construction? Had different buildings behaved the same way in the tremor or had there been subtle but important variations in their responses? Unhappy over the vague categorizations in use, an increasing number of earthquake specialists began to work out more extensive charts, each containing numerous subdivisions. Each subdivision was identified, not with a general zone of damage, but with a specific, discernible reaction by designated structures and physical objects to an earthquake shock.

By the turn of the century, more than twenty different scales had been proposed and had found their way into use. However, one scale, representing largely the combined efforts of one Swiss and two Italian professors, came to be the one most favored by earthquake investigators. Over the years, the scale, which has been known at various times as the Rossi-Forel scale, the Mercalli scale, and finally the Modified Mercalli scale, has been adapted by other seismologists to conform with changing construction practices and with the emergence and use of new materials. The scale's wording, as well as some of its imagery, is broad and in places even vague. Nevertheless, its guidelines, as outlined immediately following, are still used to give laymen and scientists alike a useful insight into tremors.

I. Not felt except by a very few who might live in an extremely undisturbed environment—no vibrations from passing cars, refrigerators, or other machinery.

II. Felt by only a few persons who are resting, especially on upper floors of buildings. Delicately suspended objects may swing.

III. Felt quite noticeably indoors, especially on upper floors of buildings, but many people do not recognize it as an earthquake. Standing automobiles may rock slightly. Vibrations are similar to those of a passing truck. It is possible to estimate the duration of the tremor.

IV. During the day felt indoors by many, outdoors by a few. At night some are awakened. Dishes, windows, and doors are disturbed. Walls make cracking sounds. Sensation similar to a heavy truck striking a building. Standing automobiles rock noticeably.

V. Felt by nearly everyone. Many are awakened at night. Some dishes, windows, and other glass objects are broken. In some places, there is broken plaster. Unstable objects are turned over. Trees, poles, and other tall objects are visibly disturbed. Pendulum clocks may stop.

VI. Felt by all. Many frightened and run outdoors. Some heavy furniture moved. Some instances of falling plaster and damaged chimneys. Other damage slight.

VII. Everyone runs outdoors. Damage is negligible in buildings of good design and construction, slight to moderate in well-constructed buildings, considerable in poorly built or badly designed structures. Some chimneys broken. People driving cars notice shaking.

VIII. Damage slight in specially designed structures; considerable in ordinary substantial buildings, with some suffering partial collapse; great in poorly built structures. Panel walls torn out of frame structures. Chimneys, factory stacks, columns, monuments, and walls fall. Heavy furniture is overturned. Underground sand and mud are ejected to the surface in small amounts. There are changes, in level and clarity, in well water. People driving automobiles are perturbed.

IX. Damage considerable in specially designed structures; well-designed frame structures thrown out of plumb; damage great in substantial buildings, with

some suffering partial collapse. Buildings shifted off
foundations. Ground is conspicuously cracked. Underground pipes are broken.

X. Some well-built wooden structures are destroyed.
Most masonry and frame structures destroyed along
with their foundations; ground badly cracked. Rails are
bent. Numerous landslides around river banks and
steep slopes. Sand and mud are shifted. Water is
splashed over banks.

XI. Few, if any, masonry structures remain standing.
Bridges are destroyed. Broad fissures open in the
ground. Underground pipelines are put completely out
of service. Earth slumps and land slips in soft ground.
Rails are greatly bent.

XII. Damage total. Waves seen are reportedly moving
across solid surfaces.° Lines of sight and level are distorted. Objects are thrown upward in the air.

The Modified Mercalli scale, still favored today for the
vivid and easily understood picture it gives of earthquakes,
has its advantages. Once an earthquake has been observed
and once intensities have been assigned to various areas
where the earthquake has struck, seismologists can plot the
areas on a map, drawing lines to connect the points where,
according to the investigation, the shaking and damage has

° Waves along solid surfaces are questioned by most, if not all, scientists. Experienced researchers have reported seeing waves move across sidewalks and concrete
floors during severe earthquakes. These same observers, however, have reported
that minute inspections of the seemingly disturbed areas after the tremor yielded
no evidence—cracks, or vestigial buckling—that would indicate that a physical
change had actually taken place where the waves had been seen. Thus, the most
likely explanation for the mysterious waves, scientists say, is that the tremor sets off
disturbances, or waves, in the fluids within the eyeballs of the observer. The physi-
ological disturbance acts on the optic nerve and is misinterpreted in the brain as
movement along the ground where the "waves" were seen. Other scientists speculate that the tremor's effects on the delicate balance mechanism in the ears lead to
the "vision" of waves.

been about the same. The first isoseismic maps (as they are called) gave seismologists some inkling about the way the forces of an earthquake distribute themselves, the effect they have on various structures, and the way in which soil conditions could either enhance the forces of an earthquake or serve as a buffer against them.

On the other hand, although every effort is made to have only trained seismologists gather information in an earthquake zone and to assign intensities to various affected zones, the scales can be nothing but subjective assessments, often too dependent on the personality of those performing the interviews and those being interviewed. "In some regions such as parts of Eastern Canada," Perry Byerly, a professor of seismology at the University of California at Berkeley, has written, "he [the investigator] may find the inhabitants proud of the shock and inclined to exaggerate the effects. In most parts of California, he finds the local people heartily ashamed and inclined to conceal or even deny the facts. . . ."

Byerly has a wide range of advice for the would-be investigator. "In the author's experience young men are the frankest [in answering questions], presumably because they own little property and are in no fear of their parents," he wrote in 1942. "It is best on making inquiries to appear important, to attempt to place the weight of some institution behind you, and not casually inquire at the roadside as though curiosity were the motive."

The Modified Mercalli intensity scale does a fairly good job of describing the effect of earthquake forces. It cannot, however, define the forces themselves, the way in which these forces are distributed, and, ultimately, the mechanism responsible for the generation of the destructive forces. For this kind of knowledge, seismologists had to develop sensitive instruments that could detect earthquakes, pin down the exact time of their occurrence, and measure the vibrations they induce within the earth. The instruments also had to have the capability to make permanent, accurate records that could be examined and reexamined.

Probably one of the earliest attempts to develop a seismometer (Seismometers merely detect an earthquake. Seismographs are seismometers that detect earthquakes but have a mechanism that records the vibrations received.) was made in China in the second century after Christ by a man named Chang Heng (Chōkō in some other accounts). Chang Heng reasoned that earthquakes had to have a point of origin and that, given an appropriate device, he would be able to determine from where the earthquakes that sometimes rocked China were coming. The artistic conceptions of the "seismometer" Chang Heng developed vary, but an essential outline emerges. The base of the instrument was a huge, hollow sphere, some eight feet in diameter. From it sprang a long, narrow neck, about eight feet tall. Eight dragon heads ringed the neck, their yawning mouths precariously holding a small ball. Beneath each one of these monsters, Chang Heng had fashioned a frog head, each one slanted upward, its mouth wide open. Inside this somewhat awesome display, the Chinese experimenter suspended a swinging shaft that, hopefully, jostled by the shaking of an earthquake, would hit one side of the tall neck, jostling one of the balls from the dragon into the mouth of the frog below. A quake to the east, theoretically, would displace a ball on the west side of the instrument. It was, for the times, a nice try, but far too simple an instrument to deal with the complicated and diverse ground motions set off by an earthquake.

The first crude but scientifically worthwhile seismographs were developed in the late 1800s, when scientists hit upon adapting, with one major exception, the principle of the pendulum for use in their earthquake-sensitive machines.

A pendulum in and of itself is nothing more than an interesting demonstration in physics. If a mass is suspended from a fixed point and if force is applied, the mass will swing through an arc. The pendulum's movement in this arc is controlled by the momentum applied, the length of the pendulum, and by the mass's response to gravity. That is, the mass acts almost like a rock thrown out of a window. Just as the rock's travel downward is controlled by gravity, so the pendulum's swing through the arc is controlled by the mass's response to gravity. Putting pendulums to work, Galileo found that they could be made to move with such regularity that they could be used to control clocks. More recently, prospectors in search of valuable ores have used highly sensitive pendulums to trace potential lodes. As prospectors walk around a site where mineral deposits are suspected, the deposits of ore, concentrated along certain areas, change the gravitational pull around them, thereby setting off slight differences in the pendulum's movement.

In a normal pendulum device—a clock, for example—the bob, or mass, of the pendulum, set in motion by force, swings while its base remains still. A seismograph, however, is so designed that when an earthquake strikes, the pendulum moves only *after* its base, anchored firmly to the ground, has been displaced by the force of the tremor. In other words, the first noticeable effect of an earthquake on a seismograph (if we were to observe the machine in slow motion) would be a movement in the shaft, or base, from which the mass hangs. Then, there would be a change in the inclination of the string or wire connecting the bob, or mass, to its base, an inclination proportional to the amount by which the ground has been shaken away from its original spot. In time, of course, the bob, or mass, follows the movement.

A pendulum device is still not enough to provide adequate data for successful seismological observation because a pendulum's reaction to force is not always on a one-to-one basis. Long, slow force applied to a pendulum will have almost no effect if the wire holding the mass is short. If you attach a weight to a piece of string and move your hand back and forth slowly, you will find that you may get very little, if any, swinging reaction from the pendulum. Only as you increase the size of the string, will the mass begin to swing back and forth in response to long, slow hand movements. Thus, if the vibrations coming from the earth are of a long, slow duration, a simple pendulum would have to be unmanageably long to record them. A vibration of ten seconds would have a measurable effect only on a pendulum nearly eighty-four feet long.

As a result, the developers of the early seismographs had to find some way of keeping the wires short without seriously abridging the swinging period of the pendulums they wanted to use in their instruments. Thus, seismologists developed seismographs in which the pendulum, suspended from a wire, was also attached to its supporting column by a boom, which itself was joined to the support by a universal joint that allowed the boom to move like a swinging gate. Placing the support into a not quite vertical position was equivalent to lengthening the wire, an artifice that allowed seismologists to have a pendulum that would swing as long as they thought necessary without lengthening the wire itself. In this way, they could have a wire barely eight inches long that would enable a pendulum to attain a swinging period of ten seconds.

Merely refining and miniaturizing the pendulum was not sufficient to give seismologists an all-purpose instrument. In an earthquake, vibrations hit from all directions. But because the seismographs worked with a mass that was attached to a solid boom, itself attached to a supporting pillar, the reactions of an individual pendulum, and therefore of the seismograph, were limited. If a swinging gate points to the east, it will move only if it is pushed (by wind or human hand) from the north or south. If the gate points to the north, it will react only to forces coming from the east or west. Similarly, a seismograph with a boom pointing east, will react only to vibrations coming in from the north or south. A seismograph with a boom pointing north, will react only to vibrations from the east or west. Thus, early seismograph stations needed three machines: one with a boom pointing north or south, one with a boom pointing east or west, and one with a boom so placed that it would react to forces moving up and down. Only in this way could all the forces of a quake be recorded. But as seismologists gained knowledge, they designed seismographs that did away with the primitive and separate pendulums, substituting one machine with one heavy mass—sometimes a sphere, sometimes a rectangle or square—to do the job of three pendulums. The mass, supported by one to four springs, hinged to just one vertical rod (springs and rod deployed according to the fancy of the designer), could move in any direction necessary.

The more intricate mechanisms presented their own problems to be solved. For example, when an earthquake strikes, it does not set off just one set of vibrations. Rather, it sets off an entire series, much like a stone thrown into water sets off a concentric series of ripples. A seismograph would be of little use if it were to be set in motion by the first incoming vibration and were to continue moving in reaction only to it, paying little attention to the succeeding set of disturbances making their way toward the instrument. To work around the natural tendency of the seismographs to respond only to the first arriving vibration, seismologists worked out methods that would allow the instruments to recognize every incoming vibration, record it, and then be prepared to meet the next one. In some machines, for example, this was done by designing the instrument so that the motions of the earthquake are made to drive a small vane through oil or through a narrow opening. Either method serves to dampen the motion of the pendulum or weight once the vibration causing the motion has been recorded and to allow the mass to return to its resting position to await new vibrations. In other machines, the boom or weight carries a small magnet that, in the course of the earthquake-induced motion, passes near a coil of wire. As the magnet passes the coil, it sets off an electric current in the wire. The resulting force of the electricity is enough to put a drag on the magnet and send the boom back to its starting position in time to receive the next vibration. The time involved, of course, depends on the duration of the vibrations.

The actual recording of the incoming vibrations is accomplished in a number of ways. The simpler seismographs, for example, recorded vibrations by using a mirror attached to the pendulum. When the pendulum was set in motion by an earthquake, the mirror rotated while a beam of light was made to play off it and to focus on photographic paper wrapped around a drum. As the light hit the paper, it exposed a line whose zigs and zags corresponded to the waves intercepted by the machine. Today's more advanced seismographs use several pens to scrawl out simultaneous records on a slowly unfolding roll of paper.

Once the earthquake has struck and has been fully recorded, teams of seismologists gather the data collected on seismographs and, by studying the various records, can determine the exact time of the earthquake, its focal point (the spot within the earth where it actually had its genesis), its epicenter (the point on the surface directly above the focal point), and, by making intricate calculations, the extent of the ground motions induced by the earthquake as well as the amount of energy released by the tremor.

Once the calculations are made, the seismologists, using techniques devised by Dr. Charles Richter, now retired from the California Institute of Technology but still active in seismology circles, can assign the tremor a magnitude, a numerical value that identifies it in the eyes of the public and in the eyes of the scientific community around the world. However, to the layman, the meaning of the various Richter-scale numbers (worked out in the thirties) can be confusing. While the numbers progress in standard arithmetic fashion to a high of 9 (including decimal points: 3.5, 4.6, 6.6, 7.8, etc.), an earthquake of 4.5, for example, is not just a little bigger than an earthquake of 3.5. When the Richter scale is used by seismologists to indicate ground motion, every full step up on the scale represents a logarithmic increase in motion. That is, an earthquake of 4.5 is said to have released ground motions ten times greater than an earthquake of 3.5. Furthermore, when the scale is used to talk about energy released, the actual values talked about change even more dramatically. An earthquake assigned a 5 classification, for example, releases between thirty and fifty times more energy than an earthquake assigned a magnitude 4. An earthquake of 6, in turn, releases thirty to fifty times more energy than an earthquake assigned a magnitude 5. Thus, the largest earthquake ever recorded (near 9 on the scale) releases a million million times as much energy as the smallest earthquake. According to a calculation made by one geologist, an 8.9 earthquake releases energy equivalent to that which could move one mountain, twenty miles in diameter and one thousand feet high, two miles off the ground.

In discussing the measurement of earth tremors, we have been saying that seismographs recognize and record vibrations generated by an earthquake. But using the word *vibration* is an oversimplification, for what the seismograph is really recording is a host of energy waves: that is, energy created at the source of the tremor and propagated by surface waves that travel along the surface of the earth and

that are by and large responsible for the destruction
wrought by an earthquake, and body waves, which travel
down and through the earth, spreading throughout the
globe.

The recognition that various waves are a major product of
earthquakes helped seismologists (even though they weren't
completely sure what earthquakes really were) refine techniques for measuring the tremors. But more important, the
hunt for the waves and the constant research to devise increasingly sensitive instruments capable of detecting even
the smallest and most remote earthquakes helped scientists
describe with precision those areas of the world where
earthquakes were striking most often and gave them their
first realistic glimpses of the earth itself. Ultimately, it
helped them formulate the first plausible explanations for
the mechanism behind earthquakes.

Of the two types of waves, surface waves and body
waves, produced by an earthquake, the body waves turned
out to be the major guides to geological discoveries. What
specifically are body waves?

If we take any solid object—including a rock—and hit it
with a hammer, disturbances are set off, running through
the body of the object. An earthquake is, in essence, a giant
hammer, and when it strikes the rocks of the earth, two
types of disturbances are set off, running throughout the
globe. In one of the disturbances, the first molecules to be
exposed to the force react by pushing directly on their
neighboring molecules. In other words, the disturbance is
moved on from the source of pressure because each individual particle in the path of the disturbance moves forward
and backward. In the second type of disturbance, the first
rock particles exposed to pressure react by moving side-
ways. As they do, they pull aside neighboring particles, and
the result is that the disturbance, instead of traveling on in a
straightforward manner, travels along in shear fashion,

much like a whip snapped by a flick of the wrist. Because these disturbances in the body of the object are in essence transfers of energy and because such transfers are accomplished through waves, the disturbances are called body waves. When scientists first discovered the two disturbances, they called the push-pull disturbance a "P," or primary, wave because, when an earthquake struck, it arrived first at seismograph stations. They called the whiplike disturbance an "S," or secondary, wave because it trailed in after the P wave. That the P, or primary, wave and the S, or secondary, wave also turned out to be push-pull and shear waves, respectively, was a stroke of luck scientists seldom get as they struggle to give precise nomenclature to scientific phenomena.

When an earthquake strikes, the P wave and the S wave start off together—they are, after all, the products of the same hammer blow. However, the P wave, because it moves in a simple longitudinal manner, travels at almost 3.5 miles per second. The S wave, having a much more tortuous path, moves slower, at about 2 miles per second. Thus, by the time the two waves make their appearance at seismograph stations, they seem to represent not one, but two distinct hammer blows.

When the early seismologists started keeping time charts and grasped this fundamental difference between the two waves, they began to keep extensive records for the arrival times of the P and S waves from earthquakes striking at various distances from several key seismograph stations. Since the difference in arrival times for the two waves differed for every distance (at 500 miles, for example, the difference in arrival time is 107 seconds; at 600 miles, it is 129 seconds; and at 900 miles, it is 193 seconds), they were soon able to set up charts equating difference in wave-arrival time with distance from any station to the presumed area of the quake. Now, a seismologist studying a seismograph record need only take note of his watch and consult his handy chart to learn immediately how far away an earthquake has struck.

Pinpointing the exact site, or epicenter, of an earthquake within the country, state, or province where it is suspected to have originated is somewhat more complicated. For example, when the February 9, 1971, earthquake struck California, seismologists at the University of California at Berkeley, at the United States Geological Survey in Menlo Park, California, and in attendance at various other seismograph stations around the country were able to look at their P and S arrival charts and determine immediately that the general area of the earthquake had been metropolitan Los Angeles.

But where specifically within that sprawling zone had the epicenter been located? To determine that, the records from several seismograph stations had to be pooled. Because the stations were in separate sites, each one would show a different distance to the presumed general area of the earthquake. For example, station A, approximately 300 miles from the Los Angeles area, would yield time-travel curves showing the quake to be about 308 miles away. Station B, 600 miles from the general Los Angeles sprawl, would show time-travel curves pointing to an earthquake 610 miles away. Station C, on the other hand, 1000 miles away from Los Angeles, would show a 1007-mile distance from the earthquake. Using each recording (in reality using scores of recordings), seismologists drew circles, each describing the distance between one recording station and the general Los Angeles area. The point at which the various circles intersected pinpointed the earthquake's epicenter, a site north of the San Fernando Valley.

Studying the behavior and patterns of the P and S waves, seismologists at the turn of the century quickly refined their ability to detect and locate earthquakes. Their studies soon began to yield bonuses in the form of vital information about the earth's structure. What they learned—plus other bits and pieces of information about the behavior of earthquakes—eventually led them to viable theories explaining the mechanism behind seismic action.

In 1909, an earthquake, not particularly distinguished for either the damage or injuries it caused, rocked a corner of the Balkan section of Europe. Most seismologists took passing note of this minor shudder in a largely insignificant part of the world and then went on with other work at hand. But a Serbian seismologist, a little more concerned with something that had happened right in his own backyard, decided to delve further into the tremor.

After collecting records made by other seismograph stations, the seismologist, a man named A. Mohorovičić, arranged the readings in order of their distance from the presumed epicenter somewhere in the Croatian countryside, in the process plotting out the time-travel curves of the P wave.

When he had finished his calculations and charts, Mohorovičić stepped back to study them, and was soon struck by something quite puzzling. For much of its duration, the P wave traveled at the speeds commonly attributed to it. But then suddenly, at about one hundred miles from the epicenter, the P wave seemed to change into high gear, moving faster than anticipated and arriving at some distant stations a little faster than it should have. Mohorovičić knew his home territory, and, as far as he was concerned, there was nothing along the surface of the earth that could possibly account for the increase in the wave's speed. Thus, the Serbian reasoned, there could be one stimulating alternative explanation. Once the P waves were generated, they penetrated into the earth, traveling, for a portion of their journey, through a zone with one kind of material or rock. Then, at one point, the waves moved to a zone where they encountered a second type of rock that allowed them to move faster. This, Mohorovičić reasoned, could only mean that the earth, rather than being one homogeneous piece of rock as previously thought, was in truth divided into at least two significantly different layers.

The dividing line between the upper layer, which was labeled the crust, and whatever else was below it came to be known, in honor of its discoverer, as the Mohorovičić discontinuity. Mohorovičić's colleagues, however, were not content merely to name the newly discovered geological world, and practically stampeded to explore the crust further. Among other things, they wanted to know how thick the crust was and if perhaps it too was subdivided into layers. As new earthquakes struck with fair regularity around the globe, seismologists strove to squeeze whatever new information they could out of the seismic events.

Unfortunately, ardor and curiosity far outstripped the methodology and instrumentation available to those who wanted to follow up on what Mohorovičić had discovered. Some seismologists were using watches that were either inaccurate or out of synchronization with timepieces used by other seismologists. Thus, estimates of time and estimates of distance were often wrong. But most important, all seismologists (even those of greatest insight and ability) were handicapped because they had to depend on the capriciousness of nature to provide them with the earthquakes they needed for their studies, without, obviously, being able to control the site, depth, or energy of the tremors. The almost unavoidable result of these unrefined and uncontrolled studies was the addition of a rash of layers to the crust as one seismologist after another published his latest observations.

It was not until the days immediately following the Second World War that seismologists were able to map with accuracy the earth's crust. Besides having better instruments than their early-twentieth-century predecessors, they had one additional and vital advantage: they were able to set off artificial underground explosions. Subsidized by oil companies whose directors understood that a better definition of the crust could lead to the identification of pockets where petroleum was trapped, the seismologists could set off explosions at different sites and depths to "sound out" the crust. To check their findings, they were able to repeat explosions at any given site until they were sure their data were accurate. Thus, by the 1950s, they knew that while the crust varies in composition and thickness, it certainly does not have the vast number of layers assigned it by early researchers. Under the continents, seismologists and other earth scientists found, the crust is really a two-layered structure, the upper part composed of granitelike rocks, the lower part, basalt-type rocks. Under the oceans, they found, the granite was completely absent and only basalt graced the crust. Furthermore, in the deepest parts of the seas, the basalt itself is exceedingly thin. Under some continental mountain ranges, the crust—basalt and granite together—is estimated to be as much as fifty miles thick. Under parts of the ocean where it is at its thinnest, the basalt crust is at times only five miles thick.

The discovery that the earth had a crust was just the first bonus garnered by scientists in their work with the P wave.

Once the P waves move out of the crust, the earth researchers found, another increase in the wave speed takes place. In a way, this was not totally unexpected because scientists already knew that in general body waves travel more rapidly in rigid material, and, as the distance to the core of the globe decreases, the earth's rocks, under tremendous weight and pressure, are packed with increasing rigidity and denseness. But even forearmed with this knowledge, seismologists were temporarily surprised by yet another quirk in the P wave's behavior. All energy, including sound and light, grows dimmer and weaker as it travels from its point of origin. In a way, the P waves conform with this law of physics. As the distance between the epicenter of the earthquake and seismograph stations around the world increases, the recordings of the P wave grow fainter and fainter. The signal begins to grow particularly weak at stations about 103 degrees (1 degree equals 621 miles) from the earthquake and from there grows fuzzier and fuzzier until the P record is virtually unreadable. But suddenly at stations 145 degrees away—stations that are on an angle from the epicenter—the seismographs again begin picking up clear P-wave records, records that grow sharper and sharper at succeeding stations. In other words, between 103 degrees and 145 degrees, there seems to be a shadow zone largely free of P waves.

What accounts for these strange ongoings? Beno Gutenberg, as a young seismologist in Germany, (he was later to join the professorial ranks at Caltech), reasoned that if the area of the earth that lay beneath the crust were one solid mass of material right through to the earth's core, the P wave would indeed grow weaker and weaker, soon dying out completely. But its almost triumphant reemergence at 145 degrees suggested that at some point the P wave, rather than being allowed to move all the way through the earth and to peter out, is being reflected back to the surface, almost as if something within the earth were acting as gigantic mirror.

In essence, that "something" acting like a mirror, at an estimated eighteen hundred miles inside the earth, represented an entirely new zone within the globe. It was called the core. The block of earth that ran from the core to the crust came to be known as the mantle. And the boundary between the mantle and the core came to be known as the Gutenberg discontinuity.

The P waves, however, did not stop dispensing their surprises there. With even more sensitive instruments coming into use, seismologists found that some P waves do indeed

come out through the shadow between 103 and 145 degrees, although when they do emerge, they are greatly
weakened and delayed. If the core, as Gutenberg and others
had supposed, acts like a mirror reflecting P waves to stations at 145 degrees, what could account for the traces of P
waves at seismograph stations within the shadow zone between 103 and 145 degrees? To account for this phenomenon, a Danish seismologist, Inge Lehmann, suggested the
existence of still another zone, a core within the core. Some
P waves are penetrating the outer core, her theory ran, and
upon reaching the inner core are reflected at a sharp angle
back out to the surface into the shadow zone that had previously been considered empty or free of P-wave traces.

While groping toward an understanding of the body
waves generated by earthquakes and the clearer picture of
the earth's interior that those waves were sketching for
them, earth scientists were coming to understand—in primitive fashion—some of the events responsible for triggering
the body waves—the events within the earth that immediately preceded the earthquake.

Rocks under pressure act as if they were made of rubber.
If intense pressure is applied to rocks—either suddenly or
slowly—they expand until the pressure overwhelms their
elasticity. At that point, they break and shatter, the broken
pieces snapping back to undistended but smaller sizes. But
if the pressure is eased before the breaking point is reached,
or if the elasticity manages to overcome the pressure, the
rock, rubber-band-like, snaps back to its original shape.

This potential for elasticity has led to a partial explanation of the mechanism behind earthquakes. Tremors are set
off when rocks subjected to tremendous pressures either
break under the strain or, overcoming the pressure in some
fashion, rebound, like rubber, to their original shape. The
body waves, P and S, of course, are set off by the breaking
or rebounding action.

This apparently simple explanation, however, was not always so clear to earth scientists, and for a good reason. When laymen and scientists were exposed to an earthquake, they most often were witnesses to its secondary characteristics—narrow fissures that opened up in soil, massive landslides, even the ejection of mud and water during the most violent of the tremors. But they almost never had a chance to see the one simultaneous phenomenon of paramount importance: the rupturing, during the tremor, of massive rocks along a long, narrow area, the formation of faults that today are known to even the least geologically informed man in the street. As late as the 1950s, Dr. Charles Richter says, seismologists knew of only fifty-five earthquakes that had been accompanied by visible surface rupturing of rocks along a visible fault zone, and sixteen of these earthquakes had been in the western United States.

According to some geological historians, the first clear evidence that faulting in rocks accompanied earthquakes came during a sizable tremor in Cutch in western India. Later, in 1891, a Japanese scientist named B. Kotō spent long days and hours investigating a mammoth earthquake that had struck the Japanese provinces of Mino and Owari. By talking to the inhabitants of the two provinces and by trudging over the fields and countryside, Kotō learned that, at the instant of the earthquake, a sixty-mile-long break had scarred the rocky surface of the provinces. Roads, fences, and trees, which had formed a straight line across the area where the break had come, were now crooked. Parts of the roads and fences on the right side of the fault had been shifted off line several feet. Furthermore, the land on one side of the break had actually dropped several feet. From what he knew about other earthquakes (and perhaps the one in Cutch) Kotō proposed that earthquakes were the result of these massive tears in the rocks within the earth.

Kotō's proposal was for seismologists a radical departure in thinking. Before the Japanese had made his suggestions, from the little they did know, seismologists had assumed that earthquakes had *led to* the infrequently observed breaks in rocks, not the breaks to the quake.

Barely fifteen years after Kotō, substantial backing for his theory came when hordes of geologists and seismologists invaded California in the wake of the great earthquake that ripped through more than two hundred miles of the northern part of the state in 1906.

Among those to make the pilgrimage to the shattered countryside and cities of the state was a Johns Hopkins scientist, Harry Fielding Reid. To get a bearing on the area and on what had happened, Reid began sifting through land surveys conducted regularly in the Bay Area by the U.S. Coast and Geodetic Survey before and after 1906.

The U.S. Coast and Geodetic Survey had completed one survey between 1851 and 1865, one between 1874 and 1892, and one in 1906–7, shortly after the earthquake. In each survey, an imaginary line had been drawn (to serve as a constant) stretching from Mount Diablo, twenty-seven miles east of San Francisco, to Mount Mocho, south of Mount Diablo, thirty-three miles east of the San Andreas Fault. Studying these records, Reid saw that between the first and second set of studies, the Farallon Lighthouse, twenty-two miles west of the San Andreas Fault, had moved 4.6 feet in a northwesterly direction, parallel to the fault. Mount Tamalpais, which was located four miles east of the fault, Reid saw, had moved more than 5.4 feet in the same direction. On the other hand, between the 1874–92 survey and the 1906–7 survey, the Farallon Lighthouse had moved another 5.8 feet northwest, but Mount Tamalpais had moved back 1.9 feet. In a period of just thirty years, the Farallon Lighthouse had moved almost 10 feet in relation to the eastern side of the fault. Furthermore, Reid noted, other west-side landmarks near the fault had been displaced more than west-side landmarks farther away from the fault.

Had the 1906 earthquake never happened, the results of the surveys on both sides of the San Andreas Fault would have survived as nothing more than a minor puzzle to the U.S. Coast and Geodetic Survey geologists who had done the fieldwork. The San Andreas was, of course, well known. However, those who thought about it at all, thought of it—until Reid came along—only in light of the seismic theory dominant at the time: it was generally accepted that the fault was the result, not the cause, of scores of earthquakes.

However, when Reid dovetailed the changed positions of landmarks west of the fault to measurements taken before and after the massive 1906 earthquake, he came to a portentous conclusion: immense distortional forces had been working on the earth in the vicinity of the fault.

For a time, Reid proposed, forces were inexorably pushing the land on one side of the fault onward, in the process actually changing the land. But at some point, the forces working on the giant rocks spanning the fault exceeded the ability of the rocks to bear them. At that point, Reid said, the rocks ruptured, some of their parts snapping elastically forward on one side of the fault and thereby relieving the strain wound into them. In some areas, the resultant jump forward covered as much as twenty feet.

Reid's proposition, which he called the elastic rebound theory, went a long way to solidify the assertion made by a few that faulting was the cause of earthquakes. One puzzle, however, remained at the time and, as far as some geophysicists are concerned, has not been adequately answered to date. When a large earthquake strikes an area, it is almost always followed by a series—sometimes hundreds—of encore earthquakes called aftershocks. The first of these can sometimes be as intense as the original earthquake, although, as they go on, they decrease in size and severity until they just peter out. If an earthquake represents a successful effort by rocks to free themselves of unbearable strain, why is there enough strain left over in the rocks to cause subsequent aftershocks? Why is not all the force removed in one stroke? After all, if a piece of rubber is stretched to the breaking point, after the piece is broken there is no tension left to go *on* breaking the already fractured parts.

Some geophysicists have proposed that, in the earthquake sequence, the main tremor relieves stress placed on some rocks. However, in the very process of relieving that stress, the main tremor shifts some of the strain over to other rocks that were not pressured by the original accumulating stresses. Now, faced with unbearable strain, these other rocks also begin to break, setting off the earthquakes that make up the familiar aftershock sequences. The pattern of shifting strain and stress continues until the smallest rocks, susceptible to smaller and smaller strains, have finished breaking.

Other geophysicists have proposed that the manner in which the stress is put on the rocks may have something to do with the pattern of stress released in a continuing earthquake sequence. According to this theory, when rocks are strained, a great deal of the crushing comes relatively quickly, while additional pressure force accumulates slowly. When the breaking point finally comes and the rocks yield to the forces working upon them, the force pressed quickly into the rocks is released in one major shudder. Then, over a period of time, the stress that had been pressed slowly into the rock is released in a proportionally slow manner. In other words, according to this theory, rocks could be compared to a rubber ball: squeeze such a ball in your hand, and you can press one side in quickly, while additional give comes slowly and then only with additional pressure. Release the ball, and the pressed side often pops back quickly, but stops short of its normal position. Then, as the ball works to regain its original shape, the pressed wall moves out slowly, almost painfully searching for its previous position.

The evidence that accumulating stresses distort rock until it shatters gave rise to an urgent question: what formidable mechanism could be present in the earth that could possibly be responsible for applying such awesome force to rocks? For an answer, seismologists turned to basic geology. The continual erosive processes scarring the earth's face, they thought, could be the potential sources of earthquake-producing stresses.

The earth's rocks are of three categories: igneous rocks, which have been thrown or carried out of the earth's interior through volcanic action or which, solidified, stay beneath the surface; metamorphic rocks, rocks of varying origins, changed over the eons by pressures within the earth; and sedimentary rocks, stone formed by layers of sedimentation.

Of the three types of rocks, earthquake researchers were mostly interested in sedimentary rocks, which cover three-fourths of the earth's total land surface. As erosion forces ravage the earth, they constantly grind up earth exposed to them. While cold and heat often weaken already existing rocks and make them susceptible to the destructive energy of wind and water, much if not most of the erosion process is carried out by rivers and streams that grind up stone along their path and carry the ground-up material off to other areas, some hundreds and thousands of miles away. The Mississippi River, for example, as it makes its way to the Gulf of Mexico out of northern Minnesota, grinds down and carries away nearly four hundred million tons of material every year. Along the way, as a stream or river changes course and speed, various particles drop out, forming new layers of dirt. As the layers pile up, they are eventually compressed into new rocks.

As far as geologists could see, however, the bulk of material eroded out of lands and mountains on the continents was being deposited, not along the route of the river itself, but where many rivers ended their long and destructive journeys, the ocean floor near the continents. There, the earliest theories about the origin of earthquake forces said, the sediments gathered year after year, century after century. As they did, they grew in weight, in the process deforming and depressing the supporting ocean floor. According to some accounts, as the ocean floor warped under sedimentary weight it formed basins, which, over a period of twenty-five to fifty million years, deepened, perhaps at a rate of five hundred to one thousand feet per million years. As the basins deepened, it was thought, the oldest layers of sediment, the ones at the bottom of the heap, began to heat up under pressure. As they expanded under increasing warmth, they took up more and more room, until they had no choice but to ooze out of the sides of the basins, pushing upward and outward from the sea depths. Through this continuous spewing out, and the resulting tilting, bending, and uplifting in the earth's upper crust, the rocks formed new mountain ranges, but not before the accumulating strain of the process set off massive earthquakes. Thus, earthquakes were referred to as the result of "tectonic" (mountain-building) forces.

Other geologists proposed variations on the theme of erosion and mountain building as a cause of earthquakes by advancing the theory that various areas of the earth's surface —whether they held mountains, flatlands, or oceans—were really huge, individual segments of crust. The segments "floated" on the mantle and, like closely packed ice cubes of different sizes in a bowl of water, had to be in constant balance with each other. However, as erosion did its handiwork, transferring material from hill to flatland, or, more important, from a mountain top on one block of crust to ocean bottom on another block of crust, the precarious state of balance between the blocks was changed. One block, grown lighter, rose off the mantle; another block, grown heavier, sank into the mantle. As this balance changed, great stresses were thought to accumulate in the rocks of the areas that constituted the borders between the blocks. Eventually, the theory said, these stresses gave way to earthquakes.

While the theories were ingenious, the schools of thought proposing explanations for the origin of earthquake forces were as fragmented as any piece of rock after an earthquake. Some geophysicists, for example, while accepting the proposition that changes in the crust were somehow responsible for the accumulation of earthquake-inducing stresses, were not ready to accept erosion (or anything related to it) as the key source of stress.

Many geophysicists, for example, strongly felt that the sources of earthquake-producing stresses were rooted in the emergence of the earth during the creation of the solar system. The advocates of this theory, however, could agree only on general principles, but parted company on specifics —primarily because they could not agree how the earth actually had been formed. Some scientists argued that the earth had originally been a part of the sun and had been formed either by a solar explosion, which had ejected enough material to form the new third planet, or by the gravitational force of a passing star, which had managed to wrest enough material from the sun to form the earth. Thus, one school of geophysicists argued, the earth obviously had at one time been a mass of molten material. From the moment it had sprung loose, these geophysicists proposed, the earth had begun to cool, a process continuing into modern times. They felt that the outer layers had been cooling much more rapidly than those inside, and, as the outer layers cooled, they solidified and contracted. In the cooling process, stresses were set up between the various parts of the crust, accounting for the forces that caused rocks to break.

Other geophysicists argued that while the rocks inside the earth had been cooling off slowly since the earth's formation, they also were emitting radioactive heat that made its way to the surface through conduction. But even as radioactive heat made its way out, the earth's surface was receiving radiation heat from the sun. The combined sources of heat, it was proposed, served to keep the earth's surface at a fairly constant temperature and size. But the inner terrestrial material, warmed only by self-generated radiation, was nevertheless shrinking as its radiation ability ebbed. The combined result of all the heating and cooling, these scientists argued, was that the earth's interior was shriveling while the crust was not. Thus, from time to time, the crust, bound to be too large to fit the condensing layers below it, would slowly collapse. "It is this behavior," Professor Perry Byerly wrote at one point, "that is one very probable source of the elastic strain in the crust, with resultant folding, faulting and earthquakes."

By and large, no one could offer a theory that would please everyone. Some earth scientists dismissed all the heated-earth theories, pointing out that the distribution of elevations and depressions on the earth's surface just could not be reconciled with a shrinking or collapsing surface as a cause of earthquakes. Others pointed out that if erosion was a factor in the genesis of earthquakes, then great earthquakes would take place largely in the vicinity of the world's great river deltas, where the erosive processes were continuously depositing their products. But again, the evidence for this was highly inconsistent. Great or severe earthquakes admittedly had occurred at the mouth of the Irrawaddy, a river flowing through Burma to the Bay of Bengal; the Indus, which flows from west Tibet through

Kashmir and Pakistan to the Arabian Sea; and the Ganges, which flows from the Himalayas to the Bay of Bengal. On the other hand, there have been no earthquakes near the Mississippi or the Amazon, flowing from the Andes to the Atlantic Ocean. Furthermore, and most important, the rim of the Pacific Ocean—where there seemed to be a disproportionate amount of earthquake activity—was a region of moderate rainfall, small and short rivers, and an area where generally the erosion of earth from one place to another could be considered negligible.

If seismologists and geophysicists seemed to wind up in one dead-end theory or another in trying to explain the forces behind the accumulation of earthquake-producing stresses, the responsibility for the erroneous turns and twists of their thinking lay more in the inadequate technology at their disposal than in the quality of their deductive thinking. It remained for the paranoid-inspired technology of the cold war—combined with the reemergence of a 350-year-old theory and some intuitive thinking—to give earth scientists their first really satisfactory explanation of some of the secrets behind the trembling of their planet.

Chapter Two

When the early Spanish, Dutch, English, Portuguese, and French explorers returned from their daring travels to the New World and around the globe, they dumped hoards of gold, silver, fine textiles, and exotic spices at the feet of their sponsoring sovereigns. On the way out of the throne room, they stopped by the local cartographer's office and dropped off what sketches and measurements they had made of the new lands they had visited and passed.

As the mapmakers painstakingly put together the information given them and outlined the edges of the continents, they, and a few scientists of the day, were struck by the jigsawlike configurations that seemed to suggest that if the land masses on opposite sides of the Atlantic Ocean could be pressed together, they could compose one great land mass. As early as the seventeenth century, in fact, Sir Francis Bacon publicly proposed the possibility that the western hemisphere had once actually been joined to what was Africa and Europe.

The intriguing idea was revived almost two centuries later when another scientist, Antonio Snider, was struck by the similarity between American and European fossil plants dating back almost three hundred million years, an observation that led him to espouse the theory that perhaps all of the globe's continents had once been a solid land mass. Snider was soon joined in his ruminations by an Austrian geologist named Eduard Suess, who, having studied the correspondence of geological formations in the southern hemisphere, proposed that they had once fitted together in a single continent he christened Gondwanaland. Finally, in the early part of the twentieth century, two other scientists, Alfred L. Wegener, a German, and F. B. Taylor, an American, independently suggested that all of the world's continents had once been a massive unit that had broken and drifted apart over millions of years.

Despite bitter protestations from Taylor's disciples, Wegener has come to be recognized as the foremost exponent of the drifting-continent theory. According to Wegener's viewpoint, the primeval unicontinent (he called it Pangaea) was a single land mass as recently (geologically speaking) as 135 to 200 million years ago. Then, for some still undetermined reason, the huge land mass began to rupture, South America breaking away from Africa, the tear spreading northward until North America split off from Europe. Antarctica, Australia, and India eventually began a separatist movement, and India, in its breakaway, folded the continental land mass between it and what is today central Asia into the Himalayan highlands. Wegener rounded out his theory by suggesting that the continents were made of strong, or "competent," rocks of silicone and aluminum and were floating upon weaker, or "incompetent," rocks made of silicone and magnesium. As the continents floated, Wegener concluded, they set off the forces responsible for the building of mountains.

Although Wegener's ideas immediately attracted attention when he first proposed them, most geophysicists came to dismiss them as too fanciful. It took more than fifty years to prove Wegener (and by extension Taylor, Suess, Snider, and Bacon) right. And as scientific proof came in bits and pieces to confirm the validity of his theories, the experiments and observations behind the evidence also yielded an elegant explanation for the secret mechanism responsible for the world's high earthquake activity.

In the 1950s and early 1960s, geologists puzzled over a remarkable phenomenon they were observing in recordings of magnetism embedded in rocks of the ocean floor. As lava squirms out of the earth's interior, through volcanoes or other deep fissures or openings, the iron grain in the molten rock is magnetized, and as the rock cools, that magnetization is "frozen" into the rock forever. The scientists studying the ocean floor found the expected magnetization in the rocks of the ocean crust. But they also discovered that the magnetism in the rocks did not always point—as they thought it should—in a northerly direction. A sizable number of readings showed that the rocks under the waters were magnetized in a *southerly* direction. There were, in other words, deviations suggesting a flip-flopping of the magnetic field.

For earth scientists, as for most people, the constancy of the magnetic field had been one of the few unquestionable and invariable facts of life. There was a south pole and there was a north pole, the north pole's greatest attribute being that it could attract the needle in the compass of a sailor plowing through the oceans or the needle in the compass of a boy scout tramping through the woods. But in the late 1950s, scientists began proposing the theory that the magnetic field, far from maintaining a constant direction, actually reversed itself from time to time. According to geophysicists now, the north-pole–south-pole orientation has reversed itself at least sixteen times in the last four million years, the last reversal having come sometime during the last seven hundred thousand years.

When they pinned down their reversal theory, earth scientists suggested that this reversal of the field explained the magnetic variations detected in the ocean's rocky bottom.

Throughout the 1950s, geophysicists (usually young geophysicists who had little seniority and had to take the less glamorous assignments dispensed by their institutions) rode around the California coast in ships dragging magnetometers, instruments capable of reading the strength of the magnetic pull embedded in the rocks. For a time, the field reversals they uncovered could be only enigmas. But the ocean-going geophysicists got something to think about when reports came in from a Hawaiian geophysical expedition working on land. The scientists on the mid-Pacific islands had found something they thought quite remarkable in the lava flows they were studying on the sides of the islands' many volcanoes. They found that in measuring the pattern of magnetization in the rocks they were also finding patterns of magnetic reversals. In rocks several million years old, the magnetization was oriented in one direction. In younger, neighboring rocks, the magnetization was oriented in the opposite direction.

Taking the hint from the Hawaiian lava flows, some scientists suggested that the pattern of alternating magnetization in rocks of different ages might be paralleled on the ocean floor. Here too, they said, if new crust was being formed as lava oozed out of the earth's interior and into the ocean, the lava would be magnetized in one direction as long as the field remained unchanged. When the field reversed itself, the new underwater lava flowing after the reversal would be magnetized in an opposite direction. As ships with magnetometers (and senior geophysicists aboard, now that there was a scientific killing in the air) set off to crisscross the entire Pacific Ocean, the suspicion was confirmed. It was found that from the continental shelves to a vaguely mysterious area that came to be known as the Mid-Oceanic Pacific Ridge the magnetic patterns reversed themselves regularly. From the Mid-Oceanic Ridge to the west, they also reversed themselves, but in a mirror image of the reversal pattern between California and the ridge. But most important, when rock samples were cored from the ocean's floor, carbon-dating procedures suggested that the reversal pattern fell in with the estimated times for each reversal. Starting in California and moving to the ridge, the subocean rocks grew younger and younger, magnetized always in the direction of the most recent reversals. Again, on the other side of the ridge, as the ships moved farther and farther from the ridge, the rocks grew older and older.

That the newest and freshest crust lay so near the Mid-Oceanic Ridge while the older crust on both sides lay farther away raised the intriguing possibility that the ridge— which was actually a chain of towering mountain ranges and deep valleys on the ocean floor—was actually responsible for the generation of new crustal material. It was along this ridge, geophysicists thought, that crevices opened to the earth's interior, abundant supplies of hot lava.

During the 1930s and 1940s, it had become clear that many earthquakes were striking out in the ocean. And, in the 1950s, the geophysicists who had found and defined the Mid-Oceanic Ridge suggested that many earthquakes could in fact be traced to the underwater mountain ranges and valleys. This theory too was substantiated in the 1960s, when data started to pour in from the new World Wide Standardized Seismograph Network (WWSSN), a phalanx of seismograph stations deployed to detect nuclear-arms tests.

Earthquakes that were once too weak and distant to make clear recordings at the older seismograph stations were suddenly being picked up by the WWSSN in abundant numbers. When these records were studied, they confirmed that small, shallow earthquakes were very common along the Mid-Oceanic Ridge. The new data also authenticated a theory that the earthquakes were probably being triggered as the ridge pulled slowly apart. But most important, the WWSSN showed that the earthquakes were not occurring just along the Mid-Pacific Ridge. They were also occurring along ridges in the Indian and Atlantic oceans and in the waters of the southern hemisphere. It became obvious that the ridges were all part of a system that girdled the globe much like seams circle a baseball, and accounted for a full 23 percent of the world's surface, 33 percent of the ocean floor, and ran a length of more than thirty-two thousand miles. The detection of small earthquakes along the ridges, the measurements that confirmed the crust was at its thinnest along the ridges, and the fact that heat flows seemed to be higher along the ridges were all taken to be proof positive that crust formation was indeed going on along the length of the system.

The new seismograph network sustained in other ways the seismological picture some scientists had sketched. To be fair, earlier, cruder measurements had told them that the rim of the Pacific Ocean was the world's most active earthquake-prone area. The new seismograph network confirmed for them that the mid-ocean system accounted for less than 9 percent of the world's earthquakes and less than 6 percent of the earthquake energy released every year. On the other hand, the new measurements confirmed that the Pacific Ocean rim accounted for 80 to 90 percent of all the energy released in earthquakes occurring close to the surface of the earth and nearly all of the energy released by earthquakes deep within the earth.

The figures verifying the extent of earthquake activity around the Pacific's rim were particularly significant. Geophysicists had long been looking with some interest at the geological formations that delineated that great ocean's borders. They had noted, for example, that the Kurile Islands, a chain of islands off the northeast coast of Asia, together with the Kamchatka Peninsula, which runs along the Bering Sea, formed a long, gently curving arc. Outside the arc, ran a long oceanic deep, sometimes plummeting to 30,000 feet. The deep was also gently curved and ran parallel to the islands. In front of the arc, between the outer edges of the islands and the deep of the ocean, the WWSSN attested, the earthquakes struck at depths that were relatively near the surface of the earth, only about 15 to 30 miles beneath the sea floor. But when earthquakes struck to the rear of the arc, they struck at progressively deeper points the *farther behind* the islands they occurred. At the farthest points behind the arc, the earthquakes struck close to 450 miles below the surface of the earth. In other words, when geologists charted these behind-the-arc earthquakes, the tremors seemed to sketch out a plane that dipped under the continental side of the arc. It was, one geophysicist has pointed out, as if some great and powerful hand had taken a karate chop at an angle of forty degrees at the earth's surface near Kamchatka and the Kurile Islands.

Thus, as the 1960s were drawing to a close, seismologists and geophysicists had some seemingly unassociated, though highly interesting, snatches of information with which to play: new crust was being generated continuously at a ridge system spanning the oceanic floors of the earth; the ridge system, where the crust was being formed by oozing lava, was marked by shallow, infrequent earthquakes, a thin, already formed crust, and a high heat flow; near some of the continental edges, earthquakes were far more frequent and powerful than earthquakes at the mid-ocean ridges.

What could it all mean? Pieced together carefully and analytically, the data meshed to suggest a startling theory—one that could simultaneously substantiate the notion of continental drift and offer a plausible explanation for the origin of earthquakes. According to this new theory, appropriately christened the new global tectonics, the earth could be envisioned as comprising three distinct layers: the lithosphere, which included the crust and upper mantle; the asthenosphere, which extended from the base of the lithosphere to a depth of several hundred miles and which was relatively weak; and the mesosphere, which made up the lower remaining portion of the mantle and was relatively passive, inert, and strong.

The earth's crust, the new global tectonics said, is really composed of huge plates (their number is now put at six by some geophysicists, though others believe there are more, perhaps as many as twenty), each of which is from thirty to ninety miles thick. Because these plates are formed and enlarged by the crust oozing out of the mid-oceanic ridges and because this new crust, as it is added to the outer edges of the plates, pushes older crust farther and farther away, the plates are in effect in constant motion, skidding around the earth. Given the limited girth of the globe, this means that some of the plates are constantly bumping into each other, vying for the limited space available. When the plates cannot move past each other, one plate overwhelms the other, forcing it into deep trenches leading back into the bowels of the earth. Deep in the trenches, the submerged plate's crustal material is again melted and reabsorbed, perhaps readied to be added to lava flowing out of some remote ridge.

This new vision of a dynamic globe (dynamic in a geologic sense: the oozing at the ridges is at rates of one or two inches a year, the movement of the plates at rates of a few feet or miles over hundreds of thousands and millions of years) included other important vistas. According to the new global tectonics, the crustal plates are so broad that some of them encompass entire continents and large slices of the various ocean floors. One huge plate carries a large chunk of the Pacific Ocean floor—an area stretching from the Aleutians clear down to Antarctica, from the shores of the Far East over to and including a small, western portion of the state of California. Other plates are carrying other parts of the Pacific Ocean. One plate carries all of South America upon its back, while still another plate carries a substantial part of the Atlantic Ocean sea floor and all of North America, including most of California.

The new global tectonics was an ideal explanation for Wegener's ideas. It was now conceivable that at one point in history all of the earth's continents had certainly been part of one giant land mass. Then, for some still unknown reason, rifts may have opened up beneath the huge land mass, and, as portions of the crust were turned into giant conveyor belts, they took pieces of the land mass with them, opening up the oceans, putting great distances between the fragments that were the new continents.

But how did the new global tectonics explain earthquakes?

Off the coast of South America, according to the new global tectonics, the South American plate and one plate carrying part of the Pacific Ocean are in direct competition. Buckling under the force of the plate carrying South America, the Pacific plate is being forced into a trench lying near the coast of South America. As the plate is forced into the trench, it puts pressure on rocks deep within the earth. Some of the rocks, under the weight of the plunging plate, are ground down farther into the earth. Others are pushed up to the surface—a process that is forcing up the Andean mountain chain. But whether the rocks are pushed up or down, the resulting forces are building great stresses into the entire region. When the stresses become too great, rocks all along the area tear, and huge earthquakes roll across Chile, Peru, Ecuador, and other parts of the Latin American coast. As another Pacific plate carrying the fragment of California moves in a northwesterly direction, the pattern of the South American confrontation is repeated in the Far Pacific Northwest. Here, the second Pacific Ocean plate plunges into the deep, angled trench off the Kurile Islands and the Kamchatka Peninsula, triggering the earthquakes common around Alaska and neighboring points.

Along the western coast of the North American continent, the picture is somewhat different. Here, the Pacific Ocean plate with the tiny piece of California runs into the North Atlantic plate carrying a load that includes the Atlantic Ocean floor, North America, and the rest of California. No trench swallows either plate at this point, so the two meet along a common border—the San Andreas Fault. And, as the two plates come together, they form, by pooling the land they carry, the state of California. However, as the Pacific plate moves north to Kamchatka and as the North Atlantic plate moves in an opposite direction, to the southeast, friction develops along some points on either side of their border, friction that causes the two plates to stick together and also forces stress into the rocks on either side of the San Andreas Fault. Where the friction is small, the resulting stresses are small and earthquakes are slight. Where the friction is great, huge stresses are built into the rocks, stresses that can be relieved only by great quakes.

The new global tectonics does leave a number of things unexplained: the source of the force that has kept the crustal plates moving for millions of years and has kept new crustal material oozing out of the mid-oceanic ridges and toward the trenches where it is ultimately destroyed; the role, if any, of the earth's initial heat, gravitational energy, and radiation heat in the process of crust formation and destruction. While the new global tectonics emphasizes the interlocking relationships of earthquakes, faults, and trenches all along the Pacific Basin—the so-called rim of fire—it does not account for earthquakes in areas like the St. Lawrence Valley, Illinois, New York, Charleston, the Rocky Mountains, and parts of East Africa, Turkey, New Zealand, and the Philippines, where there seem to be no trenches gobbling up plates of crust or no plates or remnants of plates trying to move past each other. Nor has the new global tectonics theory, or any of the refinements that have come since it was put forth in 1968, explained the secret behind the shapes and deployment of island arcs like Kamchatka and the Kurile Island regions or just why the deep ocean ridges are deployed as they are.

If the new global tectonics elevated the San Andreas Fault° from a local California curiosity into a member of a complex, worldwide earthquake-producing network, the theory also enabled geophysicists to explain some of the fault's more provincial characteristics, the peculiarities that make it important to Californians and Californians alone.

About fifteen years before the new global tectonics found its way into the pages of the scientific journals, some geophysicists were already speculating that perhaps California was not one massive, monolithic land mass. Rather, they already suspected back then that a small part of the state, the corner closest to the ocean, may have been moving gradually northward for several million years. And although in the 1950s and in the early 1960s scientists could offer no plausible mechanism for this odd geologic behavior, they did offer proof of their assertions.

Carefully surveying both sides of the San Andreas Fault, geologists found that rocks, fossils, and various deposits on one side of the fault did not match rocks, fossils, and deposits directly opposite them, on the other side of the San An-

° The word *fault*, it must be recognized, is broad in the geological formations it covers. The San Andreas, as a boundary between two plates, is an earthquake-producing fault. But as the plates move and joust, they also force secondary breaks in the earth. These breaks are also faults. As plates move, earthquake-producing pressures are wound into these faults as well.

dreas Fault. Some sections of the land on the eastern side of
the San Andreas, for example, had volcanic and sedimentary
rocks that were between 90 and 140 million years old. But
the sections on the west side of the fault, vis-à-vis the volcanic and sedimentary sections, were of highly complex metamorphic rocks that were only 80 million years old. The
corresponding volcanic and sedimentary rocks on the western side, which should have matched the 90- to 140-million-
year-old samples from the eastern side of the fault, were a
hundred or more miles away. Similar discrepancies up and
down the fault, some investigating geologists felt, meant
that one side of the San Andreas had been displaced, in
comparison to the other side, about 10 miles within the last
several million years, 65 miles within the last 12 million
years, 225 miles within a period of 40 million years, and
about 350 miles in the last 135 million years. (Given the rate
of movement, it is conceivable that, in time, Los Angeles, on
the side of the fault that is moving northward, will be San
Francisco's next-door neighbor.)

For a time the geophysicists who subscribed to the movement theory (though they did not always agree on the total
distances the western side of the fault had moved or the
time it had taken to undergo its travels) were pretty sure
that the land on the west side had moved by jumping forward a few feet at a time every time an earthquake shook
the land. During small, moderate earthquakes over millions
of years, they felt, the wandering side of the fault had
shifted forward two or three feet at a time. During the hundreds of great earthquakes similar to the ones that ran
through California in 1857 and 1906, the land had jumped
forward as much as fifteen to thirty feet at a time.

But this view of sudden earthquakes as the only propel-
lants for the large mass of land received a serious setback in
the late 1950s and early 1960s.

In the middle of the 1950s, two investigators, Karl Steinbrugge and E. G. Zacher, found themselves confronted by an enigma: a barely new warehouse, part of a winery near the town of Hollister in northwestern California, was being mysteriously damaged, and, while there were no apparent or hidden soil instabilities affecting the warehouse's foundation, some of the walls and floors of the warehouse had been distorted and displaced almost ten centimeters in the eight years the building had been in use.

Steinbrugge and Zacher found that the winery building had been constructed directly over the San Andreas Fault (the main building of the winery now proudly sports a plaque announcing that the vineyard is on the fault and has been declared a "registered natural landmark" by the Department of the Interior). The only explanation of the damage, then, could be that land on one side of the fault was slowly creeping past the land on the other side of the fault. In the process, the slowly moving land was taking along the part of the building constructed upon it. Stunned by the revelation, seismologists and geophysicists began to look more closely at other parts of the San Andreas and other faults for further signs of the mysterious creep. Over the next ten years, they found that creep was also responsible for throwing sidewalks out of line in Hollister, for moving underground tunnels crossing the Hayward Fault in Berkeley, and for distorting fences, bridges, and other features dotting part of the California landscape.

Thus, in time, several things became apparent. Land on one side of the San Andreas Fault was moving forward by leaps and bounds when small and large earthquakes hit along its traces and, when small creeps tickled it, by a centimeter or two at a time. And, according to the new global tectonics, these movements—quakes and creeps—were rooted in the migration of one of the Pacific plates to the north. Where there was friction between the Pacific and North Atlantic plates, stress was triggering the earthquakes.

Where, for some still unfathomed reason, the two plates did not clash, sections of the Pacific plate just rolled on at their unhurried rate as new crust added on somewhere out in the Pacific pushed the plate on its way.

But the revelations that movement along much of the San Andreas and other faults was a combination of sudden earthquake-induced jumps and slow creepage—both fueled by the plate movements—were only gross insights into the behavior of the San Andreas Fault. Finer and closer inspections were to yield refinements in the knowledge.

When geologists, pursuing the trace of the San Andreas Fault, plunged into the Carrizo Plain, a vast desertlike piece of tortuous, semibarren land stretching through fifty miles of the central part of the state, they came across 130 small streams whose channels, crossing the San Andreas Fault, have been offset by right lateral slip. (The entire San Andreas Fault is marked by right lateral slip. That is, if one stands on either side of the fault and looks across it, the features on the other side of the fault appear to have moved to the right.) In forty of these streams, geologists found that the channels appear to have been offset to the right between twenty and fifty feet. Near those streams with considerable offset, there were some streams whose channels had been disturbed only slightly. A few other streams, also near those that had been greatly disturbed, were not affected by the fault, and crossed it in a straight line.

Since the Carrizo Plain was heavily hit by the earthquake on the San Andreas Fault near Fort Tejon in 1857, a quake in which some sections of earth on one side of the fault jumped forward nearly thirty feet, the existence, side by side, of streams with small or no offset and streams with gaping offsets would seem to be a contradiction. One current theory is that, even in an area only fifty miles long, the San Andreas Fault does not act in a wholly consistent fashion. The fault, geologists explained, is divided into segments.

Among the segments and *within* the segments, offsets
caused by earthquakes apparently can differ widely.

The vision of the San Andreas Fault as a fault of highly diversified features sharpened even further as geologists
looked deeper into the creep phenomenon. They noted, for
example, that an area running from Fort Dix to Cholame
was free of creep. Whatever offsets had occurred in the
stream channels in this area seemed to have been wrought
by earthquakes in several sudden jumps. But north of Cholame, the picture changed dramatically. Between Cholame
and Parkfield, the next town immediately to the north, they
detected the creeping action along the fault, a creep that increases in "speed" as the distance to Parkfield decreases. In
addition, they found that the creep, over the small distance
between Cholame and Parkfield, is characterized from time
to time by moderate earthquakes. Between Parkfield and
Hollister, farther to the north, the San Andreas Fault seems
to engage in creeping action that also appears to get
stronger as the distance from Parkfield to Hollister decreases. Near Hollister, in fact, the creeping action is so
strong that it sometimes comes to nearly a full inch every
year. At the same time, the area between Parkfield and Hollister is rocked by frequent but very small earthquakes.
From Hollister north past San Francisco, geophysicists
knew of strong earthquakes. They were, however, able to
detect no creep.

As the outlines of creep and earthquake activity along the
fault's trace have been fleshed out, the facts have raised
more questions than they have answered. Assuming that
strain is being built into the fault along the full 650 miles of
its course, what different roles do creep and earthquake
play in the release of that strain? Why are some sections of
the fault blessed with only a mild creep and small to moderate earthquakes while other sections suffer only occasional
but massive earthquakes? And, in light of the creep, the
great earthquake that hit southern California in 1857, and

the great earthquake that devastated the northern section of the state in 1906, what can Californians expect from the San Andreas Fault in the years to come?

Some geologists have argued that the immense strain that is built into the length of the San Andreas Fault as the Pacific plate and the North Atlantic plate move in opposite directions was relieved in the southern part of the state in 1857 and in the northern part of the state in 1906. Those great earthquakes, these geologists proposed, left the area in between—the area from Hollister to Fort Dix—relatively unaffected. In other words, with strain relieved in the extreme northern and southern parts of the state, the Hollister-Cholame sector was left out of step. Thus, some geologists say, the current combination of creep and small to moderate earthquakes in the fault's midsection represents the fault's efforts to bring this area its share of strain-free stability. According to this theory, Los Angeles and San Francisco already have had their share of earthquake Götterdämmerung originating in the San Andreas and do not have to worry about quakes from this source for a substantial length of time.

Most seismologists do not believe that stress and strain have been substantially relieved in the northern and southern sections of the San Andreas and that only the middle sector has to worry about stress-relieving earth tremors. A more likely—and ominous—explanation advanced points out that near Los Angeles in the south and just above Hollister, near the San Francisco area in the north, the San Andreas Fault is marked by sudden, sharp turns in its direction. Thus, as the Pacific plate, the western edge of California, is pushed slowly northward by the production and addition of new crust in mid-ocean, it moves easily until it runs into the severe dogleg near Los Angeles—an outcropping in the edge of the North America plate. Suddenly, the part of the Pacific plate near the jog in the road is caught, brought to a grinding halt, while the rest of the plate, away from the dogleg, keeps moving along. Pressure on the rocks caught in the bend grows greater and greater until finally, in a massive earthquake resembling the 1857 Fort Tejon tremor, the border areas of the plate plunge forward to catch up with the rest of the crust.

But why only the creep and minor earthquakes between Cholame and Hollister? One likely explanation may be that once the Pacific plate is past the jog in the road near Los Angeles, its edges then meet little or no opposition as they border the North Atlantic plate in the central part of California. Thus, for the most part, the movement here is unimpeded and can proceed as slow creep. Only when the plates, for some unknown reason, generate some excessive friction, thereby putting some stress into the rocks along the fault's central portion, do the small, occasional tremors strike.

In the northern sector of the San Andreas, the pattern that marks southern California is repeated. Another sharp turn stops movement on the edges of the Pacific plate, resulting in vast accumulations of strain.

It may very well be that the massive roadblocks to the Pacific plate's free movement in the southern and northern sectors of California have played a key role in the formation of other faults that are considered part of the San Andreas fault zone. Thus, in the southern part of the state, the Imperial Fault, which broke to the surface in 1940, and the San Jacinto Fault, which some geologists consider the most active fault in the San Andreas zone, may represent efforts by the Pacific plate to find new stress-free routes around the southern obstruction. The net result of this search, however, has been the establishment—in addition to the Imperial and San Jacinto—of several other subsidiary faults and the consequent extension of the San Andreas's influence over hundreds of miles of southern California. In the north, the efforts of the Pacific plate to move past obstructions there have resulted in similar subsidiary fractures, including the Hayward Fault, and a similar breadth of influence.

In fact, as far as some seismologists are concerned, the bends in the San Andreas Fault may even be responsible for earthquakes on minor faults not directly connected to the San Andreas complex. For example, since the fifty-mile bend near Los Angeles serves as a formidable obstacle to the Pacific plate's movement, stress may always be building up all along the landscape, not just along the border of the plate. Thus, in some areas, the driven plate may be trying to overcome barriers in its path by simply jumping over, not around, land that is in its way. The most recent outcome of this tempestuous geological behavior, some seismologists say, was the February 9, 1971, earthquake in Los Angeles— an earthquake in which land and rocks jammed forward, raising the San Gabriel Mountains almost four feet.

Despite the progress that has been made in analyzing and defining the San Andreas, geophysicists and seismologists are still far from agreement about all aspects of the fault's behavior, history, and scope of influence.

Some scientists, including Dr. Don L. Anderson, director of the Seismological Laboratory at Caltech, believe that the main trace of the San Andreas Fault may itself actually be two different faults, one formed twenty-five million years after the other, each one marked by a different rate of movement and different modes of behavior. Others, including Dr. Robert Nason, of the U.S. Environmental Science Services Administration's Earthquake Mechanism Laboratory in San Francisco, are far from certain that some of the historical and geographical time spans attributed to the fault and its movements are correct. "We still have to find out if the fault is twenty million years old or eighty million years old or older or younger," Dr. Nason says. "Some of us also favor the idea that the San Andreas Fault may be only one-third of the boundary between the Pacific and Atlantic plates. It could be that the entire zone may go as far east as the Rockies. It may be a fault zone one thousand miles wide, responsible for earthquakes in Utah, Arizona, Montana, and Colorado, not just California."

PART II

How the Land Is Made
Treacherous

Chapter Three

The two-lane narrow highway that is Skyline Drive threads its way up the San Francisco Peninsula, skirting some of the West's lushest valleys and hillsides. On a typical day in northern California—cool and heavily overcast—from points high on the drive mist can be seen quietly rolling along and through the closely packed treetops of the valleys farther down. From time to time as the road dips down into the valleys, the fog spreads its shroud over the narrow asphalt, opening just in time to afford the driver a quick glimpse of curves disappearing into yet another thick stretch of trees and foliage.

As the drive pushes north toward San Francisco, it breaks out of the wilderness, dissolving into the jumble of roads that mark the area's thickly—and becoming ever more so—populated areas. The sides are littered with shopping centers, supermarkets, and gas stations. Just south of San Francisco, the continuation of Skyline Drive also makes its way along low-lying, softly rolling hills. Here, the hills—some a

part of Daly City and its satellites—are covered by an end-
less carpet of homes—hundreds of houses, spaced but a few
feet apart, stretching into the horizon, dipping up and down
like stalled roller-coaster cars. Marred by the onslaught of
civilization, the hills of Daly City have nothing in common
with their untouched brothers to the south, save one thing:
all were fashioned by, and mark the trail of, the San Andreas Fault.

Twenty-five years ago, Daly City, small and virtually
rural, was the home of nine thousand persons. Today, ex-
ploded by population pressure, spread in every direction by
uncontrolled land development, the city holds nearly seventy thousand people—many of whom live within feet of
the San Andreas Fault.

To the immigrants who poured into the area from other
parts of California and the United States, Daly City offered
inexpensive homes (Inexpensive at the time. Even homes
bought for $28,000 ten years ago will bring $38,000 today.)
in an area that was close to San Francisco and near the
ocean. Few who rushed into the burgeoning city worried
about the proximity of one of the most dangerous faults in
the world. "We've given it some consideration, but it
doesn't bother us to a large extent," says Ivory Jones, a die
setter who lives within two blocks of the San Andreas with
his wife and sixteen-month-old son. "We weren't told the
San Andreas was so close when we looked at the house, but
even if we had we would have still bought it. We got a nice
deal on it and it has a good view."

"When we bought our house," Mrs. C. F. Hickerson says,
"we knew it was near the San Andreas and sometimes we
think about it. We wonder whether we would do the things
they tell you to do during an earthquake, like stand in a
doorway and not run outside, or whether we would panic
and leave the city. But generally it's something you just put

out of your mind and hope science will find a solution for you."

Science has not found the answer. And while a good alternative solution to the problems posed by earthquake faults would be to keep people, homes, and buildings away from the faults, it is an answer that has eluded public officials as successfully as earthquake control and prediction have eluded scientists.

In early 1970, the Los Angeles County Board of Supervisors, led by Kenneth Hahn and encouraged by the Department of the Los Angeles County Engineer, passed a stringent ordinance setting forth the circumstances under which land on or near two of the potentially most dangerous faults within the county's borders—the Newport-Inglewood Fault and the San Andreas Fault—could be developed.

The ordinance was tough and to the point. If the county engineer ruled that any site slated for development fell within the boundaries of the potentially active zones of the two faults, the developer would have to submit geological and engineering reports to the county, outlining those parts of his property that could be struck by fractures of the surface during an earthquake in the fault zones. The submitted reports were to include assessments of the magnitude of ground shaking that could be expected during an earthquake and engineering recommendations for constructing buildings to withstand the estimated shaking.

The Board of Supervisors also ordered the County Engineer's Office to maintain maps, open to public inspection, detailing the presumed locations of the Newport-Inglewood and San Andreas faults. Prospective purchasers of land near one of the two fault zones, the board hoped, would check the maps to ensure that the lot they wanted was not on or dangerously near a fault trace.

To make absolutely certain that a purchaser of land on or

near either fault zone would be warned of the potential earthquake hazards, the new ordinance required the current legal owner of a piece of land to sign a waiver absolving the county of any responsibility should his property be destroyed in an earthquake or should anyone on the property be killed or injured during the tremor.

The waiver was to have served a double purpose. It was a precaution against a growing willingness of the courts to disregard the time-honored argument that damages, deaths, and injuries resulting from natural disasters are unavoidable and liability-free "acts of God." An increasing number of courts are holding governmental bodies financially responsible for the damages suffered by private individuals in some natural disasters. More important, the waiver, which would have been attached to all deeds to earthquake-fault-threatened properties, would have served as a strong warning to potential buyers to reconsider their interest in the property.

The new ordinance—numbered Section 310 in the complicated Los Angeles County Building Code—was widely hailed as an astute piece of land-use legislation. "It was one of the most realistic and best earthquake-hazard-control ordinances introduced anywhere," says Dr. James Slosson, a private Los Angeles consulting engineering geologist. But if Kennéth Hahn and the rest of the Board of Supervisors, then County Engineer John Lambie, and the county geologist, Arthur G. Keene, thought that they had struck a blow for reasonable land use in Los Angeles County, they had but a short time in which to savor the fruits of their progressive outlook.

When the ordinance passed, little, if anything, was heard from anyone along the Newport-Inglewood Fault. The area, after all, had been filled with new and modern construction long before Section 310 passed. Few property owners, therefore, would feel threatened by moves to bring the land surrounding the Newport-Inglewood Fault under closer scrutiny for potential earthquake problems.

The quiet along the Newport-Inglewood fault zone was soon lost in the sound and fury that came rolling over the San Gabriel Mountains from a largely undeveloped area loosely known as the Antelope Valley. There, land developers had been waiting for years to capitalize on an expected population boom. During that wait, they had been able to forget that one two-mile-wide and sixty-mile-long stretch of prized land—from Pearblossom on one end to Elizabeth Lake and Lake Hughes on the other end—coincided all too well with the course of the San Andreas Fault through the northeastern corner of Los Angeles County. The narrow stretch of land is not far from Fort Tejon, the site of the great 1857 earthquake (a fact they also managed to ignore).

The people who own Antelope Valley land and who had hoped to raise a new city and suburbs there might have received the news of Section 310 with some equanimity had all been going well for them in other respects. But in fact, nothing had been going well, and the area, which many expected would eventually hold the state's second largest city, was foundering in the throes of an economic and environmental crisis.

Many of the hopes in the Antelope Valley had centered around the continuing growth of the local aircraft industry and the development of a huge jetport to accommodate the increasingly heavy air traffic over the busy southern California area. In the early 1950s the Air Force had opened final assembly and testing facilities in the area and had leased them to the expanding aircraft companies. Although the Antelope Valley was still sparsely populated at the time, employment soon climbed to the ten-thousand job mark.

As the volatile economy of the 1960s began to take its

tolls, however, employment began to skid, plummeting until only fifteen hundred persons were drawing paychecks instead of unemployment payments. When the Palmdale jetport was grounded by lawsuits filed by environmentalists concerned that its impact on the area's ecology had not been amply studied, the prospects for building almost 125,000 homes and apartment units for all those new immigrants began to fade quickly.

Thus, the next to last thing the Antelope Valley real estate interests wanted were new county rules and regulations tightening circumstances under which they could sell land and build homes. The last thing they needed was Art Keene, the county geologist, and his host of "textbook geologists," as one real estate man called them, supervising those new regulations. The real estate interests had already had too many traumatic confrontations with Keene before Section 310 had come along. The combination of Section 310 and Arthur Keene, they felt, would mean unavoidable bankruptcy.

In the 1950's, repeated heavy rains and floods had devastated the hillsides of Los Angeles, setting off landslides that destroyed or seriously damaged hundreds of homes. In response to the year-in, year-out destruction, Los Angeles City and Los Angeles County began to deal with the nonearthquake geologic hazards of the mountainous and hilly seaside region. The Board of Supervisors and the City Council passed ordinances requiring developers to hire professional and accredited geologists to study building sites and to outline areas where landslides—earth slippage, the ordinances called them—might occur. To supervise enforcement of the new ordinances, the city and the county each organized small divisions, or sections, staffed by geologists, some of whom had engineering backgrounds, and gave them the power to review and appraise the geological reports submitted with applications for building and development permits.

At the time, the real estate interests grudgingly put up with the landslide-controlling legislation because the county had tucked its overseer, the Geology Section, neatly down in the bureaucratic cellar. The Geology Section should have been made an autonomous division, integrated directly into the County Engineering Department's upper-echelon hierarchy. There the section's decisions might have carried great weight. Or at least it should have been placed under the Engineering Department's Division of Building and Safety, where it would have had a direct voice in decisions to grant permits for the construction of homes and apartment and office buildings on hazardous county land under county supervision. Instead, the Geology Section was placed under the Engineering Department's Design Division, a group responsible for the county's drainage problems. Because of its position well down in the organization, the real estate interests thought the Geology Section's decisions would be open to reversals, especially if political pressures —applied through individual supervisors—were brought to bear on those in the bureaucracy above the Geology Section.

The developers and builders, however, did not count on Art Keene's accession to the control of the section and Keene's highly conservative and restrictive views on development of land subject to all geological hazards. Before Section 310 was passed, Keene had no explicit legal tools to control development of areas where earthquake faults might threaten property and lives. To make up for the dearth of enabling legislation, Keene simply extended the Geology Section's mandate to prevent "earth slippage" in landslides to include threats posed by earthquake faults. Keene simply interpreted "earth slippage" to mean *any* dangerous land movement, including land slippage induced by seismic activity. As long as he had been ordered to control the hazards posed by moving earth, Keene reasoned, there was little rea-

son to concentrate on land moved by landslides and to ignore land moved by strong earthquakes.

If the real estate interests were surprised at Keene's imag-
inative interpretation of the law, surprise turned to anger as
it became increasingly clear that Keene and his department
were especially conscious of the potential problems posed
by the San Andreas Fault, especially as it ran through the
Antelope Valley.

Before Section 310 was passed, for example, Arthur Wallace, president of the Antelope Valley Chapter of the Building Industry Association, wanted to build a two-story family
home at Lake Hughes, an area where other homes had
mushroomed in earlier years without a great deal of objection from the county. Yet, Keene's geologists, Wallace com-
plains, raised constant objections to his building plans, in-
sisting that Wallace determine whether or not a trace of the
San Andreas Fault ran through the property before they
would give him the required approval for a building permit.
Wallace was puzzled and angry over the Geology Section's
attitude—even though professional engineering geologists
Wallace had hired as consultants could not give him unqual-
ified support for his plans. One private consulting geologist
told Wallace that while he could build on his lot, "the site
appears to be situated immediately adjacent to one of the
shears of the San Andreas fault zone. . . . It must be recognized and realized that the San Andreas rift zone is active
periodically in certain locales . . . it must be recognized
that this . . . area . . . could be subjected to a severe seismic shock as would some one hundred plus residences along
this area north of the lake. From the obvious width of the
San Andreas rift zone trending through the Lake Hughes
area, it is very obvious that the underlying rocks of the proposed construction site have been fractured as a result of
this proximity."

Wallace is not the only one who failed to sway the Geology Section's determination to use landslide legislation to control land use along the San Andreas zone. A few miles southeast of Lake Hughes, another developer had to struggle for two years to win the Geology Section's approval for plans to build 200 homes on a sixty-acre area. In the 1950s, before the Geology Section and Art Keene had come along, a spokesman for the developer said, the company had been able to lay out fifteen similar projects in the Lake Hughes–Elizabeth Lake area without the slightest opposition from the county. But before this last two-hundred-home subdivision was finally approved, the developer had to "retire" fifteen lots Keene's section said might be endangered by the presence of some of the San Andreas Fault's subsidiary traces. "It was strictly speculation that those traces were there," one of the partners in the development firm said. "But on our money, they speculate."

A third proposed development, more than any other project in the Antelope Valley, served to earn Keene the unremitting hatred of the Antelope Valley real estate interests: the Manzanita Hills Park project, a scheme undertaken by a group of investors from Hawaii and California (including some Los Angeles Dodgers) to turn nearly one thousand acres in the Lake Hughes–Elizabeth Lake area into a subdivision holding four hundred permanent homes, two hundred mobile homes, a shopping center, and recreational facilities.

Manzanita Hills Park is in an area where the San Andreas Fault seemingly disappears. That is, traces of the fault zone have been detected on both sides of the proposed development. But because no one had ever looked before, no one could say with any certainty whether or not traces of the San Andreas ran beneath the one thousand acres.

Despite the developer's bitter protestations, Keene announced that the Geology Section would not approve a development permit until an exhaustive examination had verified the absence of faults beneath the development site.

While movement on a fault trace outside the development would give buildings a severe shake, movement on hidden faults beneath the development would almost certainly tear buildings apart. The possibility that this could happen had to be thoroughly explored.

According to Arthur N. Etz, one of the prime investors in Manzanita Hills, he and his partners spent nearly thirty thousand dollars on the geological explorations they felt the county had unfairly imposed upon them. Their explorations, Etz said, had yielded no sign of the fault traces Keene insisted had to be found. Furthermore, Etz pointed out, 360 feet below the property the Los Angeles Water Tunnel runs through the proposed development site. The tunnel, he said, has never suffered any damage at the hands of the San Andreas Fault.

As far as Etz was concerned, Manzanita Hills Park and other projects in the area were the objects of a monstrous and unwarranted persecution, and he and his syndicate fought bitterly to have Keene and one of his geologists, Richard Ramirez, called off. Ramirez, Etz complained bitterly in a letter to the county engineer, "has spent a disproportionate amount of time studying the San Andreas, and is striving desperately to be regarded as an expert on it, altho [sic] there are alleged to be at least seventy other known faults in the Los Angeles Basin which merit study."

Etz's position found little favor with a number of Engineering Department officials (including Lambie) and no sympathy in the Regional Planning Commission, a watchdog agency for development in the Los Angeles County area. The consensus was that no construction could be allowed in Manzanita Hills before the status of the San Andreas Fault in and around the project had been determined to everyone's satisfaction.

Lambie (and Keene) had good reason to stand fast. That the Los Angeles Water Tunnel had not been damaged by the San Andreas Fault, they said, was hardly reassuring. The water tunnel, they pointed out, had been built after the 1857 earthquake, the last time seismic activity had hit the area. The argument that building was safe in the area because no quake had struck in the area was dismissed as well. "Just because the milk train has not come by in the last ten hours, it does not mean it won't come by in the next fifteen minutes," says consulting geologist Henry Neel. "There is going to be a quake on the San Andreas sometime and it is going to be one ring-tailed son of a bitch when it does come."

More important, Keene and others felt, much of the thirty thousand dollars Etz's syndicate had spent on geological explorations was spent in the course of finding one or two geologists—out of a parade of consultants—who would tell the syndicate what it wanted to hear and who would write reports that would be favorable to the development and would slip by the Geology Section.

Thus, consultants who warned that traces of the San Andreas might run beneath the property were roundly ignored. Instead, the developers trotted out geologists who were suspect—not because they were incompetent, not because they were perjuring themselves, but because they were simply not trained in the intensive exploration necessary to prove or disprove the existence of fault traces where those faults may be well hidden.

"What they did," says Douglas Moran, a leading engineering seismologist and an earthquake-safety advocate, "was to go out and get a retired petroleum geologist who wrote a generally favorable and wishy-washy report, and the county turned it down. The developers and the geologist screamed, 'What do you mean the report is not adequate, what is adequate?' Obviously they shouldn't have to ask. It's like a physician asking what an adequate physical examination is."

Stung by these collective experiences with the county's Geology Section and horrified by the specter of even more power accruing to Keene under Section 310, developers, property owners, and builders in the Antelope Valley rebelled.

Organizing themselves into the Antelope Valley Real Estate Committee, representing the Elizabeth Lake Chamber of Commerce, the Leona Valley Improvement Association, the Palmdale Board of Realtors, the Foothill Board of Realtors, the Juniper Hills Commerce Association, and the Pearblossom Chamber of Commerce, the real estate interests descended with force upon their representative on the County Board of Supervisors, Warren M. Dorn, who had been off on a tour of the Far East when Supervisor Hahn's earthquake ordinance sailed through the Board of Supervisors. Under Dorn's prodding, the Board of Supervisors did a complete turnabout, rescinding the ordinance virtually overnight.° "The original 310," one of Dorn's assistants said later, "turned out to be tremendously damaging to property owners and amounted to condemnation of their land. It sounded as if they needed a little more arbitration to get something people could live with."

Arbitration aimed at writing a substitute ordinance began almost immediately after Section 310 was rescinded. Representatives from the Antelope Valley committee began meeting with Lambie and other representatives from the Engineering Department's Division of Building and Safety. But the Geology Section was never consulted during the meetings. The prestigious Association of Engineering Geologists (AEG), a storehouse of vital earthquake and land-use information, was asked for advice only after a substitute ordinance had already been drafted and was ready for a vote by the Board of Supervisors.

° In the 1972 election, Dorn lost the supervisor's seat he had held for sixteen years to an opponent who had charged, among other things, that Dorn had been overly responsive to the desires of special-interest groups.

Despite thinly disguised threats that Section 310 could force developers to do business in other, less restrictive counties and that the increased costs of meeting new standards would raise home prices or force builders to cut corners during construction, the real estate interests made no appreciable progress until John Lambie left Los Angeles County to accept a new position with neighboring Ventura County. Lambie had entered the negotiations willing to achieve some compromise to soothe the real estate people. But, as the county's top engineer for fifteen years, deeply entrenched in his office, protected by civil service regulations, he had been in a strong bargaining position. He could have withstood pressures and held out for terms that would have helped the county protect potential homeowners in the Antelope Valley.

However, when a new man, Harvey T. Brandt, assumed Lambie's job—and Lambie's place at the bargaining table— he stepped into what could at best be called a bad political situation. Brandt, who had been chief deputy to Lambie, found himself in the negotiations while he was still in the traditional six-month probationary period preceding every final civil service appointment to a new office. As a result, he was caught between two powerful supervisors, Kenneth Hahn and Warren Dorn, on opposite sides of the earthquake-ordinance question. Either supervisor could, if displeased by Brandt's performance in the negotiations, have led the Board of Supervisors to block Brandt's permanent appointment. "He was," as one county official said, "highly vulnerable."

With Lambie out of the way and Brandt walking an exceedingly unsteady tightrope, the way was clear for the Antelope Valley Real Estate Committee to force the drafting of a substitute ordinance that was largely ineffectual, if not totally impotent, in the face of the problem it was meant to attack.

The real estate representatives pressed their argument that any new ordinance to replace Section 310 should not single out any particular fault by name. People had been living near the San Andreas for three generations without problems, they argued, and to mention the San Andreas was to imply that its dangers are greater than those of any other fault. The implication, they said, was unfair and discriminatory against those with property in the area. County officials, however, had included the names of the San Andreas and the Newport-Inglewood faults because they are unofficially recognized as the most dangerous in the county. "When we drew up the ordinance we didn't want to include every dinky little line that was put on a map to represent a fault," John Lambie said recently. "So we went to Caltech and asked them what the most dangerous faults are. They said the Newport-Inglewood and the San Andreas, so we wrote those in to begin with. But we planned that as surveying of faults in the county progressed, we would add other faults, found to be dangerous, to the ordinance." Thus, the "discrimination" against property owners and builders along the San Andreas would have been short-lived. Even if mapping had not progressed rapidly enough to put all property owners along other faults under the same restrictive legislation, the fact remains that the San Andreas fault zone must be considered an imminent threat. The zone represented as good a starting point toward land-use control as could be desired. The argument that one hazardous zone should not be closed to development because it is no more dangerous than any other similar zone elsewhere, in effect, begged the question. "It's like saying that people get killed on American highways and people get killed in Viet Nam, so why restrict fighting in Viet Nam if you are not going to restrict driving," one geologist who favored Section 310 fumes. Nevertheless, the specious arguments against naming names carried the day, and specific references to the Newport-Inglewood Fault and the San Andreas Fault were omitted from the draft of the substitute ordinance.

Once they had managed to strike the names of the San Andreas and Newport-Inglewood faults from the substitute ordinance, the real estate interests worked hard to limit the explorations the Geology Section could require under the new law. Ironically, the Geology Section had earlier provided the real estate people with the ammunition they needed.

In the course of earlier debate over the Manzanita Hills project, one of the private geologists hired by the developers suggested that if the county wanted property owners to establish the various traces of the San Andreas fault zone in the Lake Hughes–Elizabeth Lake area, developers should be allowed to use topographic maps based on aerial photographs of the fault. The county, backed by several experts including map makers, had rejected the Manzanita Hills syndicate's suggestion. The last time the San Andreas had broken violently enough in southern California to bring subsidiary traces through the surface of the Antelope Valley had been in 1857. Obviously, there had been no airplanes available at the time to take to the air immediately after the event to take aerial photographs of the new fractures along the fault zone. Some aerial photographs of some fault traces (where the ground would in all likelihood move and rupture again in the next earthquake) had been made since 1928. But one hundred years of erosion had been at work on some other traces, and the best way to accurately establish the course of all the traces of the fault, the county argued, would be through careful examination on and below ground. Trenches fifteen to twenty-five feet deep and several hundred feet long would be essential to confirm the presence or absence of the dangerous fault traces through the proposed site of development.

In the discussion over aerial photographs, county geologists had made what turned out to be—in the later negotiations over the substitute ordinance for Section 310—a strategic mistake. Hoping to nail down their argument against the reliability of topographic maps based on aerial photographs, the Geology Section pointed out that a pen or pencil line drawn on a map to represent in scale a fault trace would actually represent an area on the ground at least two hundred feet wide. In other words, if a map were studied as a guide to the location of a fault trace, the trace itself could be two hundred feet removed—in either direction—from the line shown on the map.

Remembering this one objection to the use of topographic maps to establish the course of the San Andreas Fault through Manzanita Hills, the Antelope Valley representatives adapted it to their own purposes. If the actual site of a trace on the ground could be two hundred feet to either side of a line drawn on a map, the developers said, then the costly trench explorations for the fault trace should be limited to two hundred feet to either side of the map line. If the fault could not be found within four hundred feet of the spot shown, the thinking went, then obviously the trace did not exist.

The by now harassed county representatives, anxious to salvage what they could for the substitute ordinance, gave in to the demand of the real estate representatives and— much to the disgust of most experts, including engineering geologists—accepted the proposal that trenching be limited to 200 feet to either side of a suspected fault trace shown on a map. Warnings by experts, including the USGS, that a 200-foot limit on explorations was "inappropriate" were forgotten. A 200-foot limit would do nothing to find a fault trace 210 feet from the spot shown on the map. It would certainly do nothing to help uncover a fault trace that might exist somewhere on the property completely unsuspected. Even before the county had managed to indulge itself in a sigh of relief over managing to force hazard-seeking exploration on land within four hundred feet of the San Andreas Fault, the Antelope Valley committee began a successful campaign for further reductions in the area subject to examination. By the time the new substitute ordinance was in its final draft and had been approved by the Board of Supervisors in the fall of 1971, developers were required to submit exploration reports on land within a thin fifty feet to either side of a suspected fault trace. Furthermore, the new ordinance said, explorations did not have to include anything more extensive than a shallow trench dug to a maximum depth of five feet and a width of one and a half feet. If the trace was not found with the highly limited search, it was presumed not to exist.

When the "negotiations" were over, the Geology Section had lost almost every scrap of power it fleetingly had to force adequate appraisal of earthquake hazards on a development site near the San Andreas. Under the substitute ordinance, Keene no longer even had the power to accept or reject a report submitted by a developer's private consultant. The requirement that a warning—in the form of a signed waiver of responsibility—be placed on the deeds to potentially hazardous land was also deleted from the new earthquake ordinance.

In 1970 then, the Board of Supervisors had started out to make a commendable effort to instill some rationality into the use of land bordering on earthquake faults. By the fall of 1971, all they had managed to do was create a theater in which they and the Engineer's Department could make a great show of concern over earthquake safety while authoring and approving a hollow, ineffective earthquake ordinance. "Strange as it may seem," Keene says dejectedly, "we were in a stronger position with an ordinance that didn't mention earthquakes at all and just talked about earth slippage. I suppose I could still bluff my way through, but I just don't have the support anymore. New housing will probably be built right across unmapped active traces of the San Andreas Fault."

Keene is not alone in mourning the scuttling of Section 310. The Association of Engineering Geologists—whose members jokingly say that they have been called the "greatest make-work outfit since the WPA" for their support of regulations that call for the exploration work they are most qualified to conduct—strongly objects to the substitute earthquake ordinance. The association's members would undoubtedly have benefited from the more stringent measure requiring their extensive geological expertise and ability to determine the effects of geological hazards on buildings. But the potential financial gains they might have found detract little from the validity of the objections AEG members have raised. A five-foot trench, engineering geologists point out, probably would be of little help in uncovering fault traces, especially in land covered with deep, loose soil deposits. Trench explorations limited to within fifty feet of a suspected fault trace are less than useless since the actual fault trace could be hundreds of feet removed from a spot shown on the map. Property buyers, whether explorations are done or not, the engineering geologists say, should be warned that the land they are being offered may be dangerously near an earthquake fault trace. "Any buyer who is looking out in that area should be made aware of the problems," Dr. James Slosson says. "There are people who prefer to live with the earthquake hazards of faulting rather than put up with a lot of people and pollution in the city. But if people are not able to prepare for the hazards because they don't know about them, selling that land is a fraud."

The Antelope Valley real estate dealers and builders are convinced that they were right in conducting their campaign against Section 310. "There are rift zones all over the state," Arthur Etz says. "Nobody pays any attention to them. It's just one of those things you have to live with, like a hurricane. If one comes through, you have had it, and then you go back and start picking up the pieces. But you mention earthquakes around here and everyone loses their marbles. There are earthquakes and rattlesnakes everywhere and you might as well get used to them." Adds the officer of one construction company operating in the Antelope Valley, "When anything happens like at San Fernando, the people who are supposed to protect the public become hysterical in their attitudes. An earthquake is inevitable. No one except God knows when it is going to come, and certainly no geologist or geophysicist does. About all those people can do is tell you that something is or is not a rock."

Others are not so sure. "From their viewpoint of a brief life," Douglas Moran says, talking about the Antelope Valley opponents of earthquake legislation, "the San Andreas is an inactive fault. But in its lifetime, the fault has moved hundreds of feet, sometimes ten to twenty feet in one jump. It's a keystone in the earthquake mechanism, and if there is one fault you can't rule out it is the San Andreas. It may be human to try to wish it away, especially by people who have property out there, but it has to be considered a major threat. It would be criminal not to consider it."

The battle over Section 310 is symptomatic of a malaise deeper than the Antelope Valley's struggle to engender expansion at the expense of public safety. The battle over 310 is, in a broader sense, symptomatic of the widespread failure—on the part of earth scientists and public officials—to define and map the fault zones crisscrossing the state. A layman following the 310 controversy might have as-

sumed that problems presented by fault traces could be cir-
cumvented if only their presence or absence in a developing
area is determined with certainty before construction begins. The picture is far more complicated. Even if various
traces are readily visible to the eye, their mere visibility tells
nothing about their behavior under earthquake conditions.
There are differences mile by mile (if not foot by foot) in the
way ground fractures along the same trace during an earthquake. There are fracture-pattern differences among various
fault traces in the same fault zone. And there are ground-
fracture differences among various fault zones. In one part
of the San Andreas, ground may fracture within only two or
three feet of one trace. Elsewhere on the San Andreas, the
ground may fracture over one hundred feet on each side of
another of the fault's traces. Along the Hayward fault zone,
there may be areas where a sizable tremor originating in the
Hayward Fault could fracture ground hundreds of feet to
each side of one of the traces along the fault zone.

Since experts agree that different faults and different sections of the same fault must be viewed as independent en-
tities, all to be studied and outlined before nearby areas are
opened up to population, it would be reasonable to assume
that studies have progressed in a steady fashion. It would
also be reasonable to assume that new findings about various
fault zones and their traces have been translated into a
wide-ranging, complete assortment of reliable maps to guide
the government official and the landowner toward proper
land use.

These assumptions, though reasonable, represent but
wisps of wishful thinking. Few exhaustive studies have been
conducted, and few of those carried out have led to detailed
maps. While the federal government does spend some
money on mapping projects (primarily through the already
overextended USGS, the U.S. Coast and Geodetic Survey,

and a few other federal departments), local governments have consistently rejected the appropriation of local monies for fault definition and mapping. When Dr. Beach Leighton, a land-use consultant and geologist, for example, suggested to San Bernardino County officials that an exhaustive effort should be made to plot local fault zones, including the San Andreas, the Board of Supervisors decided that there were more important things to do with county funds. And, while some study of geological hazards is being done on a state level, California has never come close to appropriating the estimated ten million dollars required for an exhaustive mapping project of the riskier fault zones riddling the state.

If various city, county, and state officials have been unwilling to strain their budgets to squeeze out the additional resources to undertake fault-zone mapping, they have been "encouraged" in that reluctance by political pressures, applied by real estate interests trembling with a fear approaching the psychotic over the merest of hints that accurate mapping could become a reality. To the real estate dealer, maps—like those few that would have been posted in the Los Angeles County Engineer's Office under Section 310—mean only one thing: that an evil spell will be cast upon his ability to sell property.

When the Los Angeles Earthquake Commission released its report on the February 9, 1971, earthquake in San Fernando, for example, it included an unofficial map (an artist's drawing, really) that had been published in an edition of the *Los Angeles Times*, illustrating the locations of some forty-two different faults slicing through the Los Angeles metropolitan area. "The map is presented to indicate the general locations of some of the more significant faults that have been discovered and identified in this part of Southern California," the commission wrote. "No representation of scientific or engineering accuracy, or of true scale, is to be inferred, nor is any implication made that all faults that may exist in the area are shown or that those presented are illustrated in their complete detail."

Yet, despite this disclaimer, the real estate representative on the commission suffered a paroxysm of outrage, taking angry exception to the inclusion of the *Los Angeles Times* map in the report. In a minority (of one) dissent, included in the commission's report, he scored the inclusion of the newspaper illustration. "By the commissions [*sic*] own admission the map is highly inaccurate as to scale because many of the lines shown represents [*sic*] faults as small as one (1) inch in width or as wide as several hundred yards for others, with no indication of identification to this differential," John M. Grindle, president of the American National Realty Company, wrote. "As a result this map could in the eyes of the unsophisticated or in the administration by the pompous small-time bureaucrat become an instrument of inverse condemnation of land. Regardless of all the qualification attendant in written word on the map the inprint [*sic*] on the human mind of the map as shown will prevail."

Grindle's dark fears that a map printed as a newspaper illustration would become the tool for expropriation proceedings might seem exaggerated. Other real estate interests, however, have taken the same approach and have fought, with great success, to suppress the few maps carefully researched and developed. According to Dr. Charles Richter, a seismic probability map of the United States, prepared for the U.S. Coast and Geodetic Survey as far back as 1948, was officially retired in 1952 because allegedly it would have been "subject to misinterpretation and [was] too general to satisfy the requirements of the users." But, as Dr. Richter has pointed out, the same could be said of almost any scientific work prepared for public use. Dr. Richter maintains the action was taken not as a result of "scientific criticism, but as a result of pressure from a busi-

ness group. . . ." The threat of legal action, Karl Steinbrugge, a leading expert in earthquake-hazard problems,
adds, "has reportedly kept some geologists who were familiar with the location of the Hayward Fault from publishing
their knowledge in detail."

With little or no money trickling down to support adequate mapping efforts, California's earthquake experts—geologists, geophysicists, seismologists, and engineers of all
persuasions—have been reduced to acid ruminations about
the sad state of earthquake mapping while attending conferences or sitting around lunch tables. Some practitioners are
bitter because the few maps that are in existence—USGS
maps, primarily—are far too general, they say, to be used by
engineers. These maps, the practitioners grumble, may give
some insight into various faults but do little to help the engineer assess building requirements for a specific site. The result of those mapping missions that have been carried out,
one engineer has complained, is that some geologists can do
no more than "wave their arms and say 'you can't develop
the San Andreas fault zone.' " Other practitioners complain
that map making all too often has been ceded to those less
than qualified to undertake the job. Many geologists, says
Lloyd Cluff, conduct cursory field explorations during
which they find certain features they want to believe could
have been carved out only by a fault. Often, Cluff adds, university geology departments, anxious to give their students
practical experience finding and outlining faults, send them
out on field trips into seismic and fault-ridden areas. These
students, Cluff says, sometimes return with visions of fault
zones and fault traces where in fact none may exist.
"Faults" found by some geologists and, from time to time,
university students find their way onto maps. "In many of
these cases," Cluff says, "you go out there and do an exploration with a trench and you find that the fault just isn't
there."

There have been, of course, isolated instances where public officials have managed to bring about the proper use of land around fault traces despite the absence of detailed maps. Their greatest success has come from developers who wanted to develop vast holdings of land. Generally, the developer with a thousand acres of available land will grumble when conscientious officials pressure him to avoid fault traces, but he will, in all probability, accede to governmental requests to be careful. A developer spending several million dollars to subdivide a huge site would hardly miss the additional forty or fifty thousand dollars needed to finance a thorough study of the area's fault traces. And a company with thousands of acres to fill will not find it excessively painful to juggle its plans to keep houses and vital installations off fault traces, using the scarred land for parking lots and parks instead.

"We had a developer come to us who wanted to subdivide a sizable piece of land in Fremont," Lloyd Cluff says. "At first, I outlined two fault zones for him which were about five hundred feet wide and said let's restrict it right now from development. He agreed and moved a shopping area he had wanted to place around there." In time, however, the developer came back to Cluff because the land abandoned to suspected faulting problems was too valuable —some pieces were selling at fifty thousand dollars an acre —and because the city, Cluff says, "was taxing every foot of the land, at face value, faults or no faults."

With the developer under pressure to make better use of his land, Cluff returned to the site for a more detailed investigation. "We dug about eight or nine trenches, some twenty feet deep, some five hundred feet long, and we were able to ascertain that there were three severe fault zones, eleven feet, twenty-six feet, and thirty feet wide. We mapped the zones, including faulting probabilities and the ground-fracturing effects the engineer could expect. For every zone I told the engineer the maximum horizontal and vertical faulting he could expect, including any branch faulting. Then we divided the land for allowable uses, according to occupancy and building heights. Hospitals and police stations, for example, we placed the greatest distance from the faults." The developer, "given" back some of his land, was happy to follow the new recommendations.

Some experts have suggested that the problem of recalcitrant developers could be eliminated altogether if land is "retired" long before it comes under speculative pressure. "In San Bernardino, within a mile of localities where houses have recently been built across the fault trace [of the San Andreas]," Dr. Clarence Allen says, "hundreds of acres have been withdrawn for flood-control purposes to guard against a flood that might occur every one hundred or two hundred or perhaps three hundred years. If we have the foresight and resources to guard against this kind of flooding, it seems to me that we should also have the foresight and the resources to make more realistic precautions against a great earthquake that might occur with the same frequency."

Stopping short of outright land purchases, a few municipalities have taken some steps to keep fault zones free of people and out of the developer's eye. The town of Portola Valley, a still countrified suburb of Palo Alto (and San Francisco), where homes on one- and two-acre lots are scattered among low-lying hills and are connected by winding, narrow roads, has sketched out a development plan that gives prime consideration to earthquakes. Because the San Andreas Fault cuts a 32,000-foot-long swath through the town and because the local ground was displaced 8 to 10 feet during the 1906 earthquake, development plans now call for limited and strictly supervised construction along the fault. "A similar development plan fifteen years ago totally ignored the San Andreas Fault. As a result, one strand of the fault runs beneath an intermediate school and one strand may be beneath a retirement home," George Mader, planning consultant to the town, says. "But there are some geologists living in town who work at the USGS, and one of them was the voice in the wilderness for us. No one at first wanted to pay attention to another guy waving his arms [research geologists are destined to be pictured as arm wavers by engineers and planners] about something that was going to happen in a million years. But eventually, they did listen and the general plan was changed."

Where a few jurisdictions have not been able to set aside fault-scarred land, they have partially succeeded in enforcing controls similar to those that failed to survive in Los Angeles County. San Mateo County officials, for example, resigned to the fact that land very near fault zones is already under unremitting pressure, have restricted the issuance of building permits for lots where fault traces are suspected unless the owner of the land can demonstrate, through a geologic and engineering report, that the land is safe to support construction.

On a purely philosophical basis, the question of construction within fault zones and around fault traces revolves about one point: how much protection must society afford the individual against earthquakes? There are those who would argue that no protection is necessary, that in the purchase of land, as in the purchase of any good, the only acceptable guideline is that the buyer should look out for himself. But there are those who see a fine moral point in the issue. "If an individual wants to put up a home in a fault zone, fine, because then it is his choice about where he is when an earthquake strikes," Henry Neel says. "But if you get to the point of development where you have to start putting up public schools or office buildings, you have reached the point where the resident really doesn't have a choice about the buildings he uses." If he has no choice about the buildings he uses, in an earthquake he could very well be caught—against his own better judgment and certainly against his will—in a building straddling an active earthquake trace. To mitigate circumstances in which the individual has no choice or lacks control over his environment, Neel and others say, society must face up to the obligation of severely limiting the development of housing in dubious fault zones.

Other experts take a more pragmatic outlook in their opposition to the construction of new developments along active earthquake zones. Even the construction of one individual home too close to or across a fault trace, Don Nichols, supervisory geologist for the USGS says, imposes potential burdens on the entire society, not just the individual or family who moves into that home. If an earthquake ravages a fault-straddling house, Nichols points out, the individual, who with bravado had scorned the existence of the fault, wastes no time in asking society to compensate him by giving him low government loans, financed through taxation, to rebuild his house. But most important, in constructing a house in a fault zone, the homeowner is requiring society to spend its money to build roads, sewers, and utility lines across the fault to his home. Public lifelines are expensive to build and expensive to maintain and replace. With so many fragile utility lifelines already susceptible to the power of major and minor faults, the pragmatists argue, there is little reason to add still more to be destroyed during earthquakes.

Chapter Four

As the San Andreas furrows its way through the state, its authority and power are defied at every point. The defiances do not come from only the older, established cities or from the new subdivisions and developments. The potential for destruction in the San Andreas and other faults is defied as well by the lifelines that tie urban life together—the vast and complicated network of pipes, tubes, canals, roads, power lines, and highways that bring and carry away gas, electricity, water, garbage, and people.

To some extent, government officials and engineers have made efforts to ensure that earthquake damage to public utilities and public projects will be limited. The 1964 Alaska earthquake, for example, was marked by a noticeable absence of serious fires because main electric generators were shut off by a device that moved into action at the first sign of untoward vibrations. And Alaskan gas mains were also shut off by highly sensitive switches designed to detect sudden changes in pressure along pipelines.

Hoping to avoid insuperable damage in earthquakes to come, the East Bay Municipal Utilities District, which serves more than a million persons within a 275-square-mile area of Alameda and Contra Costa counties, began a survey of its facilities in 1967, hoping to find those points in its vast network of pipes, aqueducts, canals, and tunnels that would be the most vulnerable to earthquake forces. By placing seismic maps over maps indicating the location of the utility district's various facilities, engineers found that there were a number of weaknesses in the water-supply network—mostly where the network coincided with the Hayward fault zone. Any movement on the Hayward Fault, whether creep or sudden shock, could destroy one aqueduct, a host of pipelines, pumping plants, and reservoirs. The most vulnerable part of the water-distribution network is a 3.5-mile-long concrete tunnel that runs under the Berkeley hills. The Hayward Fault crosses the tunnel about one thousand feet from the tunnel's western outlet. As a result of the extensive survey, the municipal district shored up its dams, adding sensitive monitoring and alarm devices, and stepped up surveillance and inspection of facilities. Filtering plants receiving raw water for processing were altered to include by-passes to take untreated water to alternative facilities for chlorination should the main filtering plants be damaged in an earthquake. Finally, pumping stations were reinforced with portable generators to replace machines that might be knocked out of service in a tremor.

According to state engineers, the California Water Plan, which diverts water from northern to southern California, also encompasses stringent antiearthquake measures.

The controversial plan—controversial because northern ecologists saw it as a drain on the area's water supply, which could be disastrous to animal and plant populations in the upper regions of the state, while southern ecologists saw it as another plot to squeeze more people into the already overcrowded lower regions of the state—spawned 444 miles of pipes, aqueducts, canals, tunnels, reservoirs, and pumping stations along the length of the state.

A substantial portion of the system is in conflict with major faults. The system's major aqueduct, for example, crosses the San Andreas Fault four times in southern California. According to the California Department of Water Resources, those sections of the long aqueduct crossing active fault traces were designed to absorb possible earthquake-induced horizontal movements of up to twenty feet and vertical movements of up to three feet. When they had a choice of routes for the aqueducts or pipelines, officials say, they frequently opted for those that would make the facilities more accessible to engineers and repair crews, even when those routes entailed heavy additional expense. For example, when engineers were faced with taking the system's aqueduct past the Tehachapi Mountains in the south, they had two possibilities open to them. They could have taken the aqueduct through the mountains, using a tunnel, or they could have taken the aqueduct over the mountains, using open conduits. Because either route through the Tehachapis ran afoul of the Garlock, the San Andreas, and other active faults, they discarded the idea of using a tunnel, which would have been cheaper to build but which would have placed the aqueduct thousands of feet underground. Instead, they chose the over-the-top route that would permit repair crews—in case of earthquake damage—to reach breaches in the aqueduct quickly and easily.

Designers of another public project, the new Bay Area Rapid Transit (BART), say they have taken great care to work earthquake-resistant designs into the components of the seventy-five-mile transportation network, including its long aerial pathways; underground stations and tunnels; and, between Oakland and San Francisco, the world's longest underwater traffic tube. According to engineers, the various facilities were not designed to resist completely all forces possibly released by a great earthquake on the nearby San Andreas or Hayward faults, but to "roll with the punch." In other words, in a strong earthquake some damage, perhaps even some deformation, would be expected, according to the designers, but not "objectionable permanent distortion."

While the attempts to design earthquake-resistant features into some of these public projects are commendable, their effectiveness can be considered only as theoretical. Neither BART nor the California Water Plan has been tested yet by a moderate earthquake in its vicinity. Certainly neither has undergone a great earthquake, reading upward of 7 on the Richter scale. Furthermore, just as modern-day earthquakes have pinpointed the vulnerability of supposedly earthquake-resistant construction in the private sector of the economy, the tremors have also shown that public-sector projects, some of which were also built with potential earthquake damage in mind, have been engineered and constructed under circumstances no better—in fact often worse—than those surrounding the private construction projects.

In Alaska, for example, government-owned property suffered some of the most severe losses experienced in the state during the 1964 Anchorage earthquake. In the recent San Fernando earthquake, one-half—nearly a quarter of a billion dollars—of the damage inflicted by the tremor was inflicted upon the public sector of the economy, much of it brand-new. The damage included:

> Twenty million dollars in damage to the state's extensive freeway system and nearly five million dollars in damage to the more conventional city and county roads.
> Extensive damage to five dams—the Upper and

Lower Van Norman Dams, the Paicoma Dam, the Lopez Dam, and the Hansen Dam. The two antiquated Van Norman Dams separated more than seven billion gallons of water held in the Van Norman Reservoirs from more than eighty thousand persons living directly below the reservoirs. During the earthquake, a sizable portion of one dam collapsed into the reservoir, leaving a mere four feet between the top of the water and the ragged edge of the collapsed retainer. "Fortunately, the water level was below normal at the time of the earthquake," the Los Angeles Earthquake Commission said. "It was fortunate that the heavy ground shaking lasted only about ten seconds." Had the water been at its normal level and had there been just a few more seconds of shaking, the severely damaged dam (and the second dam, which was also battered) might have given way and thousands might have lost their lives.

Seventy-five million dollars in damage to other public structures—not counting hospitals, dams, and highways—owned by the city of Los Angeles. Extensive damage was inflicted on structures owned by the city of San Fernando, the county of Los Angeles, the state, and the federal government.

Forty-five million dollars' worth of damage to water, sewer, electricity, and telephone facilities. Much of the damage to the telephone system, which by itself suffered five million dollars' worth of damage, was centered in one local switching station, wrecked by machinery that had broken its restraining braces and had careened around the station during the shaking. The Sylmar electrical-converter station, which receives eight hundred thousand volts of direct-current power from the Columbia River and converts it to the low-voltage alternating current distributed to private users, was a shambles because converters, circuit breakers, transformers, and additional equipment were all shaken from their supports. In the western section of the San Fernando Valley, more than three hundred repairs had to be made to water mains, trunk lines, service lines, fire hydrants, and damaged water valves. In another section of the valley, fourteen hundred similar repairs had to be made. "The old water system," Dr. Samuel Aroni of the UCLA School of Architecture and Urban Planning says, "made of six- to ten-inch cast-iron riveted pipes did not have a chance."

A number of factors may work against the effectiveness of earthquake-resistant precautions included in public and semipublic projects:

Quite simply, any public project—designed, engineered, and constructed under a system that awards work to the lowest possible bidder—will also be designed to cost as little as possible. Under such circumstances it is more than likely that the specifications will include only the minimal provisions to guard against earthquake-related damage and injuries.

The contractor who is awarded a contract for a public project has to follow all the specifications in the plans. However, a low-bidding contractor may not be the best man to carry out the designs, especially the few specifications that could save a project in an earthquake.

Although private projects built for private use are regulated by codes and are subject to inspection by public agencies, projects built by many governmental agencies are not inspected by any other public body. As a result, local and state agencies that seed California with their projects do as they wish. "There has been a tendency, and there still is, for public agencies to say 'we are the engineers and we don't need anyone to tell us what to do,' " says State Senator Alfred Alquist, chairman of the legislature's Joint Committee on Seismic Safety.

Many engineers who work on public projects or on utility projects under public control are, like their colleagues in private practice, loath to learn the lessons presented by other earthquakes.

Official lethargy. Although the 1964 Alaska earthquake demonstrated the value of automatic shut-off valves on pipes carrying volatile materials, few jurisdictions require utilities and private companies selling gas or oil to install shut-off devices. In 1967, experts recommended that Los Angeles County require shut-off valves on pipelines crossing active fault traces, but no action was taken. Utility-company engineers install some valves only where they consider them necessary for efficient service.

The 1964 Alaska earthquake also brought proof that badly planned and poorly constructed highways, including bridges and spans, were highly vulnerable to earthquake forces. Yet, despite the Alaskan experience, the California Division of Highways continued paying little attention and less respect to the threats posed by the state's earthquake faults and poor soil conditions, and extended its ambitious building program without substantially changing its design criteria. Thus, even after 1964, complicated interchanges, aesthetically pleasing but fragile bridges, and long and curving spans were built to defy rather than respect the earthquake menace.

On February 9, 1971, the results of the Highway Division's less than stringent construction requirements were strewn about the San Fernando Valley. Five overpasses collapsed, one killing two men on their way to work. Seven other overpasses were severely damaged, some so badly they had to be razed. According to the Los Angeles Earthquake Commission, sections of highways were extensively damaged because fills on which they had been placed gave way. Other highway sections were ripped apart by ground deformations and surface faulting. The damage, Professor C. Martin Duke said, "was monotonously familiar with practically all previous earthquakes."

"The damage that precipitated the collapses of the bridges and spans could have been avoided by a different method of design," Professor George Housner, Professor of Civil Engineering at Caltech, told the state legislative Subcommittee on Highway Structural Safety. Two design deficiencies, he said, were obvious in the damaged structures. "One is that the design rules followed do not provide for earthquake design forces as large as those the structures actually experienced during the earthquake. The other feature involves weaknesses in design details. In some places the tie bars that surround the vertical reinforcing bars in the columns were not adequate in size or spacing to enable the columns to survive the severe overstraining it [*sic*] experienced. In some cases, it seemed to me that the supports provided to hold up the bridge spans were constructed in such a way that the spans could slip off when there was relative displacements between span and support."

Confronted by the February 9 evidence that their designs were inadequate, Highway Division officials finally learned the lessons they should have assimilated seven years earlier. "The day after [the February 9 earthquake]," one official assured the Highway Safety Subcommittee, "we doubled everything we used just as a rule of thumb." He added that while "you can't design these things like pyramids . . . you can't make them big and heavy enough so that nothing will shake them . . . we do want to put enough in here so that they don't fall down. We don't care if they are hanging there like a basket drape or anything else but we don't want them to come down. That's the reason we are tying joints together, increasing the footings, running the bars continuous so they won't pull off the concrete so that when you lose the bottom . . . the bars don't come out and the column won't fall over. . . ." And in March, 1972, the state's Public Works Department announced a five-million-dollar program to modify highway bridges and overpasses to give them greater earthquake resistance. Under the program, 126 of more than 11,500 bridge and overpass structures built in California before February 9, 1971, will be modified to meet better design specifications. Particular attention, the department said, would be given to highway structures in metropolitan areas like San Francisco and Los Angeles.

While California's commitment to dam safety has improved steadily over the years, the dams may nevertheless constitute another weak link in the state's public-works system.

Before August, 1929, the state exercised very limited supervision over less than half of California's dams. But the failure of one dam in an earthquake in 1925 and then the sudden failure of a second dam in 1928 spurred state legislation that brought dams built after 1929 under state jurisdiction. Following the collapse of the Baldwin Hills Dam in 1963, a disaster in which five persons were killed and fifteen million dollars in property was destroyed, the state's police powers over dams were extended to include old and new dams. By July 1, 1969, state jurisdiction had been extended to more than one thousand dams and reservoirs in the state.

Like their colleagues in the Highway Division, state Water Department officials took the February 9 earthquake's lessons to heart. Soon after the tremor, they ordered a reevaluation of all dams in the state. Earth-filled dams like those that were part of the Van Norman Reservoirs—that is, dams for which earth banks were deposited by controlled streams of water—officials say, will be inspected first. Earth-filled dams built with modern-day machinery and compaction methods, however, will also be reevaluated. In addition, officials say that they will also require improvements in the seismic design of new dams planned for the state, perhaps asking that their designs be tested by computers.

To some extent, however, the department's commitment to dam safety is circumscribed by the inability of many engineers, public and private, to agree on the effect of earthquake forces on dams—even dams of modern design. Many engineers and public officials, while conceding that some dams have performed poorly under some earthquake conditions, nevertheless have argued that major earth dams, some old and some new, have performed admirably in the face of dangers posed by earthquake forces. No changes in design or construction methods are necessary, they say. "The danger to sound structures near or even on an active fault may easily be exaggerated," one leading seismologist has written. "One of the water supply reservoirs for San Francisco in 1906 was the Crystal Springs Reservoir, which lay right on the San Andreas Fault, filling a depression created by previous activity there. At the time of the 1906 earthquake, the earth-filled upper Crystal Springs Dam was uninjured in spite of the fact that the fault transverses the rock forming the east abutment, in which an offset of eight feet occurred. The one hundred and forty-five foot high concrete Crystal Springs main dam was not even cracked." Others have pointed with pride to various dams that have experienced strong shaking in California earthquakes in the last fifty years (including the 1952 Kern County earthquake) without collapse. The performance of a major Montana dam, which, constructed seven hundred feet from an active fault, with-

stood a major earthquake, including a twenty-foot displacement, without collapse, some experts say, is further proof
that dams are well able to survive earthquakes.

Some state officials concede that knowledge regarding the
performance of dams in an earthquake is still far from complete. Yet in late 1971, the state and the Los Angeles Metropolitan Water District were deep into plans to replace the
destroyed Van Norman Dam with a new facility in the same
general fault-pocked area. Not one of the experts they
had consulted, metropolitan officials said, had "expressed
concern regarding the safety of the modern earth-filled
dams."

While not flatly contradicting water officials, Professor H.
Bolton Seed of the University of California at Berkeley has
warned that the construction of an earthquake-safe dam in
the vicinity of the Van Norman Dam would be a "challenge." Seed, an expert on the performance of soils under
earthquake forces, is one of the experts who has warned
that the construction of new dams, even with the best of
methods, must be taken far more seriously than it has been
to date. The cheerful accounts of dams undamaged by
earthquakes, he says, fail to mention some crucial factors,
some strokes of luck that have intervened to prevent major
dam disasters.

The accounts of the performance of the Crystal Springs
Dam, Professor Seed points out, do not mention that the
dam was serving as a raised road across the reservoir or that
the water level at the time was the same on both sides of the
embankment. Thus, pressure generated by the 1906 earthquake was, for all intents and purposes, the same on both
sides of the dam. But where there is water on only one side
of a retaining wall, the situation is drastically different.
Earthquake vibrations can force the water to ramrod the
dam until it collapses. Or the tremor's vibrations could
cause the water to oscillate furiously until it leaps over the

dam, destroying it in the process. Nor was the strong 1952 Tehachapi earthquake an accurate gauge of the ability of well-constructed dams to survive strong earth tremors. Many of the dams shaken in the earthquake, Seed says, were too far away from the causative fault to feel anything more than a weak version of the intense shaking that was felt in regions closer to the fault. And, Professor Seed says, only good fortune stood between the Montana dam and disaster. "It would appear," he says, "that there is presently no valid reason for complacency regarding the ability of well constructed embankments to withstand the effects of major earthquakes, unless they are specifically designed to do so."

Whether they keep water from ranch-style homes in a California subdivision or from West Virginia ramshackle houses built along the dried-up bed of a river diverted to pour its water into a reservoir, dams have come to represent the ultimate test of nerves in the confrontation between civilization and nature. Knowing full well that the chilling scream "the dam has broken" is always a possibility, engineers and public officials plan and build the dams when and where they want to. If the project, especially if it is within an urban area or any other populated area, is questioned, the dam builders resort to their standard retort, "the people have to have an adequate water supply." If questioned about safety standards in the construction of the dam, the engineers will reply that it is being built "with the best the state of the art will allow." When the inevitable collapse does come and men, women, and children and their homes are swept away in a torrent of water, reporters, crowding around a public official wearing an appropriately grief-stricken face or around glum engineers, ask for an explanation of the disaster. In the mumbled answer, the clearest words are usually "an act of God."

The rationalizations given for building a project in an area where prudence should otherwise bar it are the same as the justifications given for the construction of dams on questionable sites—"it is in the public interest." To be sure, the widespread failure by public officials, developers, and engineers of all stripes to expand the limits of safety is a function of limited knowledge and limited funds. But to a large degree the continual spread of highways and dams and mammoth water facilities is a function of the mentality that demands constant expansion and relentless growth. It is the shortsighted mentality that allows developments to straddle faults. It is the mentality that pushes public officials to accept—and encourage—the spread of construction into marginal areas where weak and unstable soils—highly susceptible to earthquake vibrations—provide the foundations for homes, apartment houses, and office buildings where millions of Californians spend their daily lives.

Chapter Five

The San Andreas, its subsidiary branches, and a host of other major and minor faults throughout California command a fear-tinged fascination from the state's lay and professional earthquake watchers. The obsession with construction around faults is well justified. As California's population grows, as more and more people seek to escape the crowding of the cities, as more and more homes, apartment buildings, office buildings, hospitals, highway interchanges, and thousands of other structures violate thousands of fault-scarred acres, the influence and power of faults over life and property increase accordingly.

The influence of the faults and the effects of the earthquakes they generate range far beyond the land immediately adjacent to the feared cracks in the earth. For every acre of badly used land near a major or minor fault, there probably are, far removed from the fault itself, hundreds of acres of land whose peculiar characteristics—hillsides; deep, loosely compacted natural soils; shifting mud flats;

acres of man-filled artificial land; gentle, though badly graded slopes—make them highly vulnerable to the forces unleashed by earthquakes.

Where hills and mountains are nothing but firm rock, they are not seriously affected by a distant earthquake's violence. But where wind, rain, streams, and rivers have been responsible for the creation or enhancement of the hills by laying down layer after layer of loose soil, gravel, and small rocks, earthquake vibrations need do no more than rattle the land in order to send the cohesionless soils and rocks cascading down the slopes.

In some fortuitous cases, earthquake-induced landslides, while widespread, cause little damage. The February 9, 1971, earthquake unleashed almost one thousand landslides, all distributed over remote sections of a one-hundred-square-mile area of the hilly and mountainous terrain around the San Fernando Valley.

In many cases, however, earthquakes have triggered landslides disastrous to both densely and sparsely populated areas. In a fairly remote section of northern Peru, for example, a 1970 earthquake brought flooding and landslides that killed more than thirty thousand persons.

One of the most dramatic earthquake-induced landslides came in the wake of an earthquake in the Kansu region of China on December 16, 1920. As the tremor rumbled through the region, immense slides rushed out of the hills, burying and carrying away entire villages, damming stream beds, and turning valleys into instant lakes. "The only survivors in this valley were saved as if by a miracle," two observers wrote of the events that killed an estimated two hundred thousand persons. "A husband and his two sons, whose farmstead, instead of being buried, was caught upon the back of one of the slides, carried half a mile down the valley to where it was diverted by two streams of earth coming from other directions, and, as a result of the two forces, was pushed another quarter of a mile up to a small draw.

"Not until day dawned and they crawled out to find neighboring villages obliterated, farm lands carried away or buried, streams blocked and hills of earth towering above their compounds, did they comprehend that the 'hills had walked.' It was in this Valley of the Dead that the most arresting freak of the cataclysm occurred. Two sections of the ancient, well-packed highway, accompanied by tall trees which bordered it, were cut from the line of the road following the side hill, swept hundreds of yards over the bed stream, and set intact, upon an angle on top of the loose loess."

When earthquake waves pass from solid and dense rock to loose and thick soils, the waves increase in amplitude. As a result, ground motions, set off by earthquakes, last longer, leading to a more violent shaking effect on structures the soils support. The relationship between different soils and shaking severity, which became evident when nineteenth-century scientists began to seriously study the effects of earthquakes on man-made structures, was pinned down by seismologists and construction experts studying the 1906 San Francisco earthquake.

Harry Fielding Reid, even as he was formulating his elastic rebound theory, was also busy calculating some relationships (coefficients) between estimated accelerations and the different types of ground found in the San Francisco Bay Area. Solid rock, Reid found, could be assigned a "base" coefficient of 1.0. Accordingly, the shaking-ground coefficient in sandstone was between 1.0 and 2.4; in sand, it was between 2.4 and 4.4; in man-made land, it could soar from 4.4 to 11.6; and in marshland, the shaking-ground coefficient could be as high as 12.0.° In other words, when someone is foolish enough to place a structure on marsh-

° The coefficients have been reduced somewhat since Reid, although the general principle stands.

land, that building could be subjected to ground motions almost twelve times more violent than those it would suffer if it were lodged in solid rock.

The relationship between unconsolidated soils—especially thick, deep unconsolidated soils—and destruction during earthquakes has been borne out repeatedly since the 1906 San Francisco earthquake. The 1906 tremor left ample evidence for verification of Reid's calculations and assumptions. To the north of San Francisco, Santa Rosa, where descriptions of wholesale destruction had been eclipsed by the attention focused on the devastation in San Francisco, was largely leveled because it had been built on thick, unconsolidated soil. To the south, twenty-three persons had been killed in widespread destruction in San Jose, which was also founded on thick, unconsolidated soils. As studies have grown more sophisticated, soils engineers have found that, generally, the deeper the unconsolidated soils, the greater the amplifications of earthquakes may be. Soils engineers and engineering geologists studying a moderate 1967 earthquake in Caracas found that high-rise construction was affected in various ways by earthquake energies amplified by soils of varying depth. While the height of the buildings played a role in their own destruction or damage, investigators found that, generally, buildings in the eastern part of Caracas, where unconsolidated soils were from 240 to 800 feet deep, suffered far more damage than buildings in the western part of the city, where unconsolidated soils were only 60 to 300 feet deep.

Ground made of loosely compacted soils may not only amplify earthquake energies, but may also be changed by the earthquake vibrations. If soil or sand is poured into a jar, it may appear that the material has occupied the minimal amount of space it needs. But if the sides of the jar are struck, the soil or sand often will settle and compact under the prodding of the applied force. The loosely compacted soil that is found in many areas of California may act much the same way under the prodding of earthquake forces. A building placed on such soil—or worse, a building placed partly on solid rock and partly on unconsolidated soil— would suffer serious damage or would even collapse during an earthquake.

If in addition to containing loose soils, land is also water-logged, that is, if soils beneath the surface contain a high proportion of water, earthquake vibrations can force the water-saturated soils to the surface, turning the ground into a runny, quicksandlike mass, sharply reducing the support for any structures built upon it. The phenomenon (known as liquefaction), says Karl Steinbrugge, "caused the spectacular land movements involving many city blocks" during the 1964 Anchorage earthquake. One of the more notable and spectacular examples of liquefaction came during an earthquake in Niigata, Japan, in 1964. Three blocks of apartment buildings—structurally sound and constructed to resist earthquake vibrations—survived the onslaught of earthquake energies, only to sink into the ground and tilt backward as the earth beneath them liquefied and dissolved. Some of the buildings tilted almost eighty degrees, reportedly permitting some people who were on the top floors to walk down the side of the buildings to the streets.

Efforts to plan and control land use according to the hazards posed by unstable ground and soils have been far from even. In some areas of California, control efforts are non-existent; in a very few areas they have moved forward on a cautious but hopeful level. In some places, efforts have been made, only to end in battles from which developers, consultants, and the local government have emerged badly bruised.

In 1969, Sonoma County, north of San Francisco, asked the California Department of Mines and Geology for help in outlining the county's geologic hazards. In response, the department, which had been gearing up for a study of the state's geologic hazards, provided an experienced geologist who spent much of his first year in Sonoma County, studying its general geological problems. Once the broad outlines of the county's geological risks had emerged, the geologist began to study individual forty-square-mile sections (the county encompasses sixteen hundred square miles), beginning with those sections where development was most likely to come in the immediate years to follow.

Almost concurrently, Sonoma County began asking developers to submit professionally and privately prepared geological reports on specific land they hoped to open to the public. However, county officials decided they could not afford to maintain a full-time staff of geologists to appraise reports written for developers by private consultants. As a result, Sonoma requires the developer to provide the funds with which building and planning officials can hire an independent geologist to study and appraise the private report.

County officials had ample support in their determination to tighten conditions under which Sonoma land could be developed. In the toughening stance on geological hazards, conservationists saw a handy opportunity to keep the population dispersed in area and to keep it low in numbers. If the new provisions were enforced—and conservationists were ready to ensure they would be—developers could not crowd the ugly Los Angeles–type suburbs into the area's delicate countryside. The county's own maintenance departments also stood squarely behind the new regulations. Public projects, including roads and other services, placed before geological studies were required, were being constantly damaged by landslides, erosion processes, and small tremors. The new requirements would ensure that future works would be installed with an eye to nature's capriciousness, hopefully saving the county the continual costs of repairs.

When one developer came to Sonoma with plans to turn ten thousand acres of seashore land in and around scenic Jenner Bay into a densely populated new town, the county received its first test of its determination to enforce its concern over geology.

The area picked by the developer is, in the words of one of the planners, Kalvin Platt, "a geological nightmare." Precarious cliffs overlook the ocean. Where there are no hills, there are marshes, gullies, or flatlands with deep, unconsolidated soils. While the project had many boosters in the county, officials, impressed by arguments (presented by conservationists, including a University of California geologist) that the developer's intentions took little note of the area's geological risks, rejected the initial plans for the development.

To meet the objections, the developer hired Dr. James Slosson to make a foot-by-foot assessment of the property, including the potential influence of the San Andreas Fault, which, after diving into the ocean south of Jenner Bay, runs a close parallel to the property. The developer empowered his architects and planners to take Dr. Slosson's findings into consideration when they sketched out the new town.

Dr. Slosson's study revealed so many problems (nearly one-third of the land turned out to be highly susceptible to landslides) that development was limited to an initial area of one thousand acres where geologic problems were the least troublesome. Unstable land, marshes, and gullies were marked off limits for construction and were set aside for recreational or scenic purposes. The cliffs, where property would have brought prime prices for the view they afforded of the ocean, were also set aside. "Those cliffs erode like crazy," Kalvin Platt said. "If they erode a foot a year and then you have an earthquake in which you lose twenty feet at once, it isn't going to do you much good to build eighteen or nineteen feet in back of the cliff."

To further ensure the safety of the nearly two thousand dwelling units planned for the initial stages of development, Platt "enveloped" individual lots. That is, these lots were also studied for their own potential geologic risks. And where hazards were found, specific corners avoiding the dangers were marked as the only permissible points for construction.

"Ten years ago," Platt says, "our company would have gone through a similar study, but we would have probably been overruled by the developer's marketing people. Now our approach can be pragmatic. You can't and you shouldn't build everywhere. But we also don't think that because there are problems on a piece of land you shouldn't build there at all."

That same basic "pragmatic" approach came a cropper in Redwood Shores, a development twenty minutes south of San Francisco along the Bayshore Freeway.

Redwood Shores lies on a low, sprawling area of the San Francisco Peninsula. Much of the land is marked by marshes (or former marshes) and thick layers of soft ground, simply known as bay mud. A good part of the land has been reclaimed from the sea through the use of dikes. As the San Francisco area's population has grown, a significant portion of this marginal land has come to support an increasing number of subdivisions with their inevitable, accompanying crush of people.

In the early 1960s, Redwood City and the Leslie Salt Company, which owned more than 40,000 acres of unoccupied land in the area, most of it used for salt-evaporation ponds, envisioned a far more lucrative use for the part of the salt company's land: a subdivision stretching over more than 4600 acres and housing and employing more than 60,000 persons by 1980. The city thought the new development, named Redwood Shores, would represent a rich, new source of badly needed tax monies. The salt company saw the new development, with a fair-market value estimated to reach nearly $1 billion, as a good way to "recycle" land it no longer needed for salt-producing operations.

Once the city and the salt company reached agreement on the development, Leslie Salt began to blueprint the new subdivision. In 1963, the much-heralded plans were unveiled. A first-phase development would include 2500 single homes. Town houses and garden apartments would adorn an artificial lake. A gracious commercial area would tend to the residents' material needs, while a library, built on piles and surrounded by a pond, would nurture their intellectual requirements. The first stage would also include four twenty-story buildings for those who could not divorce themselves completely from urban living. In time, it was estimated, 30 percent of the contemplated population would be living in a substantial portion of the total of twenty-five high-rise buildings planned for the full development as it slowly spread over the full 4600 acres.

Questions about the potential seismic hazards in Redwood Shores, of course, were sure to arise. The San Andreas fault zone, after all, lies five miles west of the development, and the Hayward fault zone lies fourteen miles to the east. The entire site, furthermore, is marked by weak, potentially unstable soils. To anticipate the doubters, Leslie Salt and Redwood City went out of their way to hire the most prestigious consultants in the state to study the engineering, geological, and soil problems their ambitious brainchild might encounter. An authoritative San Francisco–based earth-sciences firm, Dames and Moore, was signed on to conduct the necessary soils and geology assessments of the development site. The firm of Daniel, Mann, Mendenhall and Johnson was hired to develop construction engineering requirements. Redwood City, meanwhile, formed a high-powered

advisory board—including Dr. Hugo Benioff, Professor
Emeritus of Seismology at the California Institute of Technology; Henry Degenkolb, a leading San Francisco structural engineer; Dr. Ray Clough, Professor of Civil Engineering at the University of California at Berkeley; Dr. Richard
H. Jahns, Professor of Geology and Dean of the School of
Earth Sciences at Stanford University; and Thomas M.
Lepps, a structural engineer—to assess the reports submitted by the private consultants.

When all the work was finished—it had cost Redwood
City almost $145,000 for its share of the engineering and ge-
ological studies—Redwood Shores had, for all intents and
purposes, received the green light. According to Dames and
Moore, there was no evidence that an earthquake would
cause the ground in the area to liquefy Niigata-style or that
the land would simply slump away under the onslaught of a
tremor's energy. The Dames and Moore investigators did
say that there might very well be subsidiary faults to the San
Andreas in the bedrock, deep beneath the surface, but that
the area showed no evidence of harboring a major fault or
gave no evidence "to suggest that faults, if present beneath
the site, are active."

All in all, Dames and Moore said, there was nothing in or
about the Redwood Shores site that made it a greater earthquake hazard than any other area in California, including
parts of San Francisco itself. The advisory reports, though
exuding an air of confidence, were interlaced with warnings
that studies of individual lots on the property would still be
necessary and that stringent engineering practices would be
required. The advisory board rubber-stamped the private
reports.

If Redwood City and Leslie Salt hoped to take comfort in
the expert, voluminous reports, others were far from sat-
isfied. The Seismic Advisory Board, critics said, had been
formed only after prolonged pressure from the Redwood

City Civic Association, a private citizens' group. The critics were far from optimistic that Redwood City and Leslie Salt would consult, any more often than necessary, a board that had been formed only to silence the doubters.* Furthermore, some critics hinted, the board was just too full of men whose work as consultants and engineers in other private projects had put them on terms entirely too friendly with the consultants and engineers who had prepared the report for Redwood City. It was said that all of the men involved in Redwood Shores—consultants and advisors—shared the same viewpoints, and all had too liberal a view of land-use requirements. "The relationship between Redwood City, Leslie, Dames and Moore, and the advisory board," Dr. G. Brent Dalrymple, a USGS geologist and one of the development's strongest critics, says, "was, in my opinion, incestuous."

The opinions expressed by Dames and Moore (and repeated by the advisory board), critics felt, were far from reassuring. The opinion that Redwood Shores was no more dangerous than any other part of California was hardly an encouraging thought, given the many areas in California that already had suffered heavy damage at the hands of earthquakes. Nor were critics reassured by the consulting engineers' and geologists' recommendations regarding construction techniques and details. Given pressures to cut costs and given the vagaries of construction practices in California (see next chapter), there was little reason to feel confident that the recommendations would be followed up.

Had Redwood Shores been the child of Leslie Salt alone, the subdivision—on the basis of the extensive studies done —might have sailed on to an uneventful and on-schedule completion. The involvement of Redwood City as an active partner in the project, however, complicated matters. For

* A reasonable assumption, it turned out. The board met only twice in six years.

the city to participate with funds and manpower, permission from the state would be required. But as Redwood City worked to persuade Sacramento to approve its participation in Redwood Shores, state agencies and legislative committees began to receive a barrage of arguments against further development of the San Francisco Peninsula's low-lying marshlands.

The strongest and most effective opposition surfaced in the form of a report prepared by Dr. Dalrymple and another USGS geologist, Dr. Marvin A. Lanphere. In a long study submitted to the state, the two, speaking as private citizens, said that earthquake damage to projects on soft, water-saturated ground; bay-fill; and marshland areas "could easily be of disastrous proportions." Citing other studies, they argued that damage and destruction in any number of earthquakes—ranging from San Francisco in 1865 to earthquakes in Anchorage and Niigata in 1964—had offered ample proof that development on soft ground could court disaster. Dalrymple and Lanphere urged the state to declare a moratorium on all building until further studies on the hazards of soft and water-saturated ground could be conducted and completed.

Outraged at the charges, the Redwood Shores interests counterattacked. Pressure was brought to bear on the USGS, and the Survey's Washington office responded by reining in the two men. Employees, USGS explained with a straight face, could not make public statements bearing on geologic questions without official clearance, even when they were speaking as private citizens. A scheduled appearance by Drs. Dalrymple and Lanphere at an earthquake conference was also quickly canceled.

(Eventually, the USGS was to enter the debate officially and, ironically, would come to agree with its two gagged geologists. In late 1967, as the controversy swirled, the USGS was asked by the Washington office of the Federal Housing Administration [FHA] to prepare a proposal for an official review of the Redwood Shores project. In its proposal, USGS told the FHA that, among other things, a more rigorous examination of "faulting, shaking, ground failure, settlement and subsidence [problems] . . . is fundamental to the acceptance of many of the assumptions in the [Dames and Moore] reports on which the engineering designs are based." The USGS proposal also pointed out that in the opinion of USGS scientists—approved opinions, this time around—prior engineering studies undertaken by Redwood Shores' developers' engineers and geologists "do not define the earthquake and related hazards adequately to permit a realistic assessment of potential hazards."

"The Dames and Moore study," Don Nichols said recently, "was the most comprehensive soils and engineering analysis of a home-development project I had ever seen. But even as comprehensive as the report was, as far as we were concerned, we didn't think it went far enough in the light of the Alaska earthquake experience to define the hazards adequately. Since much of the Dames and Moore work had been done before many of the Alaska studies had been completed, we felt Redwood Shores should have been looked at again in terms of concepts developed after Anchorage.")

Redwood Shores' defenders pointed out that the two men, experts in isotope geochemistry, had no expertise in engineering geology. According to David Leeds, engineering seismologist for Dames and Moore, Dalrymple and Lanphere had misunderstood the mechanics of the Niigata and Alaska ground failures. Dalrymple and Lanphere's report, William H. Moore, senior consulting partner of Dames and Moore, told the public, was "at best foolish, at worst ignorant or deliberate distortion . . . its recommendations are unfounded and quite obviously beyond the competence of its geologist-authors. Unwarranted and unnecessary public alarm can be the only result of such pseudo-scientific pronouncements. . . ."

Dalrymple remains unimpressed by the salvos aimed at him and Lanphere. "All we said was true," Dalrymple says. "It was supported by evidence and never scientifically refuted. The incompetence charge was brought on by people who had nothing factual to say."

That two competent Ph.D.'s, researching a field related to their own, would be "pseudo-scientific" and incompetent does seem to be a strained assumption. And while some of the subtleties might have escaped the two, their broadsides at developments on soft, low-lying ground in the Redwood Shores area did raise some sensitive questions, the most serious revolving about the nature and peculiarities of the bay muds (and the man-made land placed on these muds) that characterize a good portion of the land bordering the San Francisco Bay region.

Bay mud is in essence soft, silty clay that, with its high natural water content, is weak, very plastic, and highly compressible. Because San Francisco and much of the area around it have always been highly dependent on trade, the early inhabitants of the peninsula, as well as their twentieth-century counterparts, built freely on the bay muds ringing the area shores. Because in most cases they could not build directly upon the mud, they brought in fill to pour over it before constructing the necessary buildings.

Though many experts believe that the bay muds and the fills placed over them behave no worse in an earthquake than naturally inadequate soil, or that strict engineering techniques can compensate for the weaknesses of bay mud and filled land, others are not so sure.

Dr. John Steinhart has pointed out that the salt-water content of bay muds can range as high as 60 percent of their mass. As filler is poured over these mud flats, as they are diked and developed, Dr. Steinhart says, fresh water begins to seep into the mud, replacing its salty water. In some instances, the mud's natural salts are simply leached out, leaving semifresh water behind. In other cases, both the salts and the water escape the mud, which then simply dries out. In any case, sodium, which plays an important role in the composition of the mud, is either displaced or immobilized. As a result, some think, the muddy flats are strengthened. Others, however, including Dr. Steinhart, believe that the partial or total displacement of the mud's salt component weakens the mud, depriving it of what support properties it had possessed. Not enough, Dr. Steinhart says, is really known about the changes that result in the muds or about methods that could be used to compensate for the possible loss of strength. Nor do soils engineers, Dr. Steinhart says, really know what buildings on mud flats can expect in the way of amplified ground motions, ground shaking, and possible subsidence.

Critics of construction on bay muds and bay fills also point out that much of the severe damage suffered in San Francisco in 1906 did not come in the rocky areas of Nob Hill, but in the mud-supported, lower regions of the city. While modern buildings placed on bay mud or bay fills more recently, built with newer techniques, have survived moderate earthquakes, others say, these buildings have never been subjected to the ultimate test, an earthquake as powerful as the one that rocked San Francisco in 1906.

Some experts who advocate high-rise building construction on bay muds (such as the apartment and office buildings slated for Redwood Shores) point out that modern structural engineers often do not depend on the mud alone to support the buildings. Rather, it is pointed out, piles supporting the buildings are often driven down past the mud to sit firmly in bedrock. But using bedrock may not be a good answer, the critics retort, and may in fact be an added dis-

advantage during an earthquake. During a tremor, the mud
on which a building stands is subjected to vibrations, and
the piles supporting the building will vibrate right along
with the mud. Bedrock underneath the mud will, because it
is made of a different material, vibrate at a different frequency. If the piles supporting the building are driven into
the rock, in search of additional support, some experts point
out, the piles may be subject to two different vibrations,
those of the rock and those of the mud. In the process, the
piles may very well snap at the point of greatest tension—
the border lines between the rock and the mud.

According to Karl Steinbrugge, the 1964 Alaska earthquake raised some serious questions about the performance
of buildings and other structures placed on soft soils. Steinbrugge, who is one of those who believe that these muddy
regions will perform satisfactorily under some moderate
earthquake conditions, wrote in his definitive 1968 mono-
graph, *Earthquake Hazard in the San Francisco Bay Area: A
Continuing Problem in Public Policy*:

> the Anchorage experience . . . is instructive. It ap-
> pears that liquefaction of certain types of soils, under
> vibratory forces of long duration, caused the spectacu-
> lar land movements involving many city blocks.
>
> While soil liquefaction was observed and described
> after the 1960 Chilean shock and other earthquakes,
> apparently it was not adequately studied until the
> 1964 Alaskan earthquake. This brings up the
> troublesome question of the seismic risk entailed by
> Bay fills that have been placed in recent years without
> benefit of this newer knowledge of the liquefaction
> problem. . . .
>
> Soils engineering has developed quite rapidly in re-
> cent years, including the very recent accumulation of
> substantive knowledge on the potentially major hazard

of liquefaction. However, there is still much to be learned . . . concerning the seismic risk on Bay fills, marsh lands, and other poorly consolidated materials.

In view of the earthquake hazard, he adds, "the use of engineered fills over compressible deep Bay soils for building foundations must be considered in some degree experimental. . . ."

In the wake of the Dalrymple-Lanphere report, doubts also arose over one other aspect of the Redwood Shores development (and a similar earlier neighboring subdivision, Foster City): the safety and potential performance in an earthquake of the many dikes that keep the sea away from the low-lying land on which housing has already been placed and from land earmarked for the Redwood Shores development. Some of these dikes had been in place when the 1906 earthquake struck the San Francisco area. Although there were few, if any, recorded failures of the dikes at the time of the earthquake, it has been pointed out that in 1906 the dikes had stood far from solid land, alone and unencumbered. But, as developments in the area have spread in recent years, plans have been formulated to fill in land all the way up to the dikes. Furthermore, while seventy years ago many of the dikes stood almost two hundred to four hundred feet back of the shoreline, today those dikes have become part of the shoreline and are face to face with the edge of the sea. Thus, with the sea close on one side and filled land pressing on them from the other side, some experts think, the dikes today would be subject to severe ground vibrations. Simultaneously, they would be buffeted intensely by the encroaching land and sea. In a severe earthquake, their ability to hold back the sea would be severely compromised.

As Redwood Shores became a cause célèbre in northern California, it drew attention from Washington. Federal

money, in the form of Federal Housing Administration and
Veterans Administration (VA) mortgage guarantees, was in-
volved in Redwood Shores. Both the House Committee on
Government Operations and the General Accounting Office
(GAO) were curious to find out if the charges made against
Redwood Shores were true. And, if they were, why two sup-
posedly strong federal agencies had not been able to elicit
saner city planning and land-use practices.

The General Accounting Office and the House committee
found little to cheer them. FHA, they found, had no written
criteria its field offices could use to differentiate among various subdivision developers applying for coverage by the
mortgage-insurance programs. As a result, FHA field offices
often came to contradictory conclusions when considering
insurance applications. "The FHA San Francisco office,"
the GAO said in one report, "accepted for mortgage insurance purposes an area known to be within the active Hayward Fault zone, but rejected another area because it was in
the active San Andreas Fault zone although insuring office
engineers stated that it was not possible to construct in either area homes which would be stable during severe earthquakes."

To make matters worse, neither the FHA nor the VA kept
records detailing the number of insured properties damaged
or destroyed because they had been placed on geologically
hazardous land. While the FHA had some staff members
with the engineering capabilities to inspect and assess sites,
the VA had no site engineers, and neither agency had engineering geologists on its staff to evaluate projects.° At times,
FHA offices did reject areas for mortgage insurance because
FHA technicians had advised against FHA participation.
Yet, when the FHA did turn down a development, it made

° As of spring, 1972, nearly six years after the GAO and congressional investigation, the FHA had only two men handling all geological problems west of the Mississippi. One man was a structural engineer and the other was a geologist.

no effort to notify the VA that the development had been rejected because of safety considerations. As a result, a developer who had failed to receive FHA participation in his project could apply at the Veterans Administration and receive the necessary federal mortgage-insurance participation essential to a successful development.

In considering Redwood Shores and similar projects, the House committee said in one of its reports, the FHA had

> given inadequate consideration to the problems and hazards of areas with potential geologic instability. It has no requirements that such areas be identified or that any applications in such areas receive clearance from FHA site engineers before an insurance commitment is made. It has no requirements that soil investigations reports must be submitted with each application in such areas nor that such reports cover geologic conditions of the projected site.

To make up for what they considered to be "inadequate" studies of Redwood Shores before federal funds were committed, both the GAO and the Committee on Government Operations tried to force the FHA to sponsor a new, independent study of Redwood Shores, preferably by the USGS. But the FHA, already committed in spirit and in form to the project, hemmed and hawed, unwilling to slow construction and expansion.

Thus, development in Redwood Shores Unit I continued until August, 1969, when the House committee, losing all patience, virtually ordered the FHA to cease its participation in the controversial development until reasonable re-evaluation studies had been made and all questions about the site's overall earthquake and geological problems had been answered to everyone's satisfaction. Acceding to this new demand, the FHA declared a moratorium on its program in Redwood Shores.

The suspension lasted barely a year—long enough for the FHA to make up its mind that it could ignore congressional demands and could invest its resources any way it pleased. By September, 1970, government backing was once more pouring into Redwood Shores in the form of renewed mortgage guarantees and insurance. By December, 1970, home sales—despite the flurry of unfavorable publicity accompanying the House committee investigation—started picking up again. In March, 1971, an additional $12.5 million worth of new construction was announced, and by July, 1971, the two-hundredth family prepared to move its belongings to its newly purchased home in Redwood Shores.

The year-long suspension of government participation did take its toll, however. According to the Redwood City manager, the suspension had cost the Redwood Shores Improvement District millions of dollars in tax revenues. And those few families who had moved into Redwood Shores between June, 1968, when the development of Unit I started, and August, 1969, when the FHA suspension went into effect, found that their tax outlay was soaring because no other families were moving in to help shoulder the burden of amortizations of Redwood City bonds sold to finance new streets, sewers, and other services. By mid-1969, the owner of a $33,500 home in Redwood Shores was paying almost $1525 a year in real estate taxes.

The most drastic results, however, struck the Leslie Salt Company, which had helped spawn the project. During the suspension of FHA participation in Redwood Shores, Leslie was losing almost $200,000 a month in income, a setback from which it never recovered. In April, 1971, the company announced that the subsidiary division formed to supervise the Redwood Shores development was in a position where it was unable to meet its obligations to its lenders. In early

1972, the Bank of America, prime lender to Leslie Salt in the company's efforts to build Redwood Shores, was forced to take over the bedeviled bay-shore development.

At every level of government, there is an unwillingness to deal with the pressures on marginal land. Local agencies, pressured by real estate interests and by their own search for more land to tax, look the other way when hazardous land begins to sprout new developments. Federal agencies succumb to their own special pressures. The FHA, for example, was created to help families buy their own homes. But to carry out its mission, the FHA needs funds. A substantial portion of these funds is generated by interest charges the FHA levies for guaranteeing loans. In the telescopic vision of bureaucracy, the FHA came to see the campaign against Redwood Shores as a threat to its money-making capabilities. If it was forced to turn down developments encroaching *everywhere* on hazardous land, the money brought in by interest charges would slowly shrink, ultimately curtailing its activities and its personnel. Its ambivalence toward the USGS studies was characteristic of the schizophrenic problem facing FHA: the earthquake danger to Redwood Shores was important. But the long-range implications of recognizing that threat were *much more* dangerous because they threatened the bureau itself.

Are there, then, no final arbiters anywhere who, in the interest of public safety, can objectively state that a given piece of land, prone to earthquake hazards, should not be developed?

The answer, unfortunately, is no. The public discussions regarding earthquake hazards are most often conducted by a small group of men whose knowledge and understanding of earthquakes is broad and deep. As university-based consultants, as members of one or two governmental agencies concerned with "pure" geology and geophysical problems, as highly paid private consultants, these are men who have the interest, the ambition, the financial backing to steep themselves in earthquake knowledge. They jet back and forth between Japan and Turkey, Hawaii and Alaska, Chile and Teheran to attend conference after conference to pick up the latest piece of vital earthquake information. The members of this loosely knit and unofficial group can pack off on the next available plane to whatever corner of the earth has just been devastated by an earthquake to study firsthand its effects on soils and buildings. They have access to the most modern of computers capable of making the most sophisticated of calculations once new, raw data are found and translated into machine logic.

The land-use opinions of the "pure" geologists in this group (the USGS men, for example) are, as the Redwood Shores debate points out, almost immediately discarded by government officials, by practitioners, by the public. The "pure" geologists are, in the eyes of many, compromised by their near-cataclysmic view of earthquakes. Regarded as "arm-wavers," they are all too often dismissed as fanatical geological ideologues who would gladly nail all developers and builders to the nearest nonearthquake-resistant building placed on dubious land, where they would be left to await their due in the next earthquake.

As the purists of the group are silenced, the practitioners gain ascendancy in the continuing public debates. But the practitioners are men who must make a living. When a Redwood Shores comes along—or any project where, as Dr. Steinhart put it, it is "important to distinguish between the feasibility of construction and desirability of construction" —the practitioner's view of earthquake problems is clouded by the so-called realities of life, and desirability loses out to feasibility. The question, as Dr. Dalrymple points out, "is never whether, but always, how."

Thus, the discussion invariably ends in a vote for continued development. "San Francisco is a port city," Henry Degenkolb, considered one of the state's leading structural engineers, said at one conference of earthquake experts. "Much of our economy is based on trade. This requires wharves and other facilities to be located on the waterfront where ships can be serviced. We cannot put these facilities on a hill top on solid rock. While they [would] have excellent foundations, they would be rather useless in that location. So wharves are placed where they are needed and if the foundation or geology is not ideal, the engineers cannot throw up their hands and refuse to build there."

The statement may sound logical. It is, however, essentially misleading. Perhaps wharves and storehouses have to be built on bay muds and reclaimed, artificially filled lands. But is it necessary to build fifteen-, twenty-, twenty-five-story apartment and office buildings on similar sites? Is it necessary to crowd sixty thousand people into homes and apartment buildings built on land better left to mosquitoes and waterfowl?

The danger in Degenkolb's (and similar) statements is the assumption that the real world functions along the guidelines envisioned at the countless earthquake seminars that are held every year. In the broad, generalized discussions, it is always assumed that rational public officials and rational developers will always recognize the need for sensitive soils analyses. And it is also assumed that developers will always search out the highly competent and technically skilled soils engineers to conduct the necessary analyses and to tell them where to place or not to place buildings.

But in truth, there are any number of jurisdictions in California where no soils analyses are required as a prerequisite to development. And even where those analyses are required by law, the situation is often hardly satisfactory. The demand for soils analyses has led to a growth in the number of soils engineers who make their services available to the public. Thus, when a developer needs to submit a soils report to county or city officials, rather than seek out the expensive and thorough practitioners, he can shop around until he finds the one soils engineer who will do the least expensive, most permissive study possible. In the final analysis, the bulk of soils-investigation work in California is done by the Yellow Pages nickel-and-dime soils engineer or engineering geologist. This is the man whose practice demands a high turnover of clients, the man whose practice does not allow him the spare hours to keep up with the latest nuances in his field, the man whose crowded schedule keeps him from calling Caltech, or UCLA, or Berkeley when he faces a soils problem he does not understand.

To compound the situation, few jurisdictions that demand soils analyses have the manpower to handle all the reports that are submitted to them or to assess their accuracy. And as safety-conscious as the professional organizations like the Association of Engineering Geologists are, none has considered tightening the circumstances under which people are accepted into the profession or are allowed to sign soils-analysis reports that might have a profound effect on earthquake safety.

The net result of this general abdication of responsibility is that the state's potential for death, injury, and property destruction in a major earthquake is increasing almost geometrically. Simultaneously, it is allowing the gleaming new towns, suburbs, and cities, which should be havens for earthquake safety, to propagate and spread the dangers generations of neglect have spawned in California's older towns and cities.

Chapter Six

As new construction overruns the California landscape, inundating sites of questionable stability, concern over potential earthquake disasters grows. But the debate over new construction in fault zones, marshes, and swamps has eclipsed the hazard posed by the vast pool of older buildings and projects constructed before even the minimal building-code safety standards were adopted. Old warehouses are still used for storage, but many have been converted into stores and office buildings. Dilapidated apartment houses, old hotels, and crumbling motels in the older areas of the cities provide housing for millions of low-income men and women trapped by old age or race. Quaint and much sought after Spanish-style homes provide gracious—and potentially dangerous—living for thousands. Fifty-year-old school buildings are used to educate students. "The thousands of buildings with bearing walls of non-reinforced brick, held together by sand-lime mortar, are extremely vulnerable to earthquake damage," Karl Steinbrugge writes in *Earth-*

quake Hazard. "Many of these will suffer partial or total collapse in an earthquake." In California, adds Dr. Charles
Richter, "ninety per cent of the loss of life and well over
half of the property loss [in earthquakes] has been due to
the failure of weak and improperly constructed buildings. In
California during the present century this has amounted to
hundreds of lives, perhaps a thousand, and hundreds of millions of dollars. . . . Nevertheless, the main risk to life and
property is not in the new developments; it is in our older
centers of population. Almost all the serious earthquake
damage in California has affected structures put up in
former years when there was no general adoption of building regulations, and only the most perfunctory inspection."

Every earth tremor has underlined the threats posed by
California's antiquated buildings and engineering projects.
And if the battle to forestall the dangers presented by construction in marginal areas has been hard and often fruitless,
the fight to neutralize the dangers of California's antiquities,
quaint and otherwise, has left those who have charged into
the ring with more than their share of wounds and with very
few compensatory victory banners to hoist in triumph.

Over the last few years, much of the effort to correct
earthquake hazards presented by buildings erected before
the rudimentary building codes of the 1930s went into effect
has been expended to strengthen the state's school buildings.

When the 1933 earthquake struck Long Beach, the trem-
or's prime brick-and-mortar victims were the schools in
some sections of the Los Angeles metropolitan area. Although the schools were deserted at the time of the earthquake ("Our luck in schools had defied the arithmetic,"
David Leeds says. "The United States has never had a major
earthquake during school hours."), the sight of crushed

buildings—roofs, brick walls, clay partitions, concrete blocks, all scattered on and around children's desks—was enough to move the state legislature to action. Within two months of the earthquake, the legislators had written and passed the Field Act, demanding that the most stringent engineering standards possible be applied to make new schools earthquake-resistant.

For all its good intentions, however, the Field Act was an incomplete gesture. While it set strong construction guidelines for all school buildings built after 1933, it contained no provisions to protect children attending schools built before 1933. Not until 1967—more than thirty years after the Long Beach earthquake—did the state legislature finally decide that all pre-1933 school buildings had to undergo structural inspections. If found wanting, the buildings had to be brought up to the Field Act standards set for those schools built since 1933. One year later, the legislature went even further and ordered that all pre-1933 school buildings not renovated or strengthened to withstand earthquakes by 1975 be vacated.° Local school boards were told that if they did not have the money to undertake the necessary repairs, earthquake-resistive innovations, or to build new replacement schools, they were authorized to hold bond elections to raise the necessary funds. If the electorate rejected one proposal, the board was obligated to submit another bond issue to the voters within five years.

The legislature's edicts—unaccompanied by state funds or even the hope of state aid to accomplish the dictated objectives—pushed local school boards into untenable situations. The need to raise the estimated six hundred million to

° In 1967, the legislature also plugged another Field Act loophole. The original act had set stringent engineering requirements but had said nothing about geological requirements. The 1967 law required school boards to hire geologists to assess proposed school sites to ensure that no school would fall prey to faults. For many schools, the new requirements were too late, and many educational plants, though well engineered, were placed on active fault traces.

one billion dollars required to achieve earthquake school
safety came at a juncture in time when property owners in
particular and the electorate in general were in a rebellious
mood over rising taxes, rioting students, and striking teachers. The school bond issues suddenly became the way to
punish school authorities for the alleged sins of their
charges. "We have had a lousy climate in which to try to
pass earthquake bonds," says John H. Queiser, an official of
the San Francisco Board of Education. "In addition to everything else, desegregation orders and bussing haven't
helped. Teachers have been shifted around in the desegregation orders. The union is upset. The PTA's are upset. Both
would have helped us at one time in bond elections like
these, but this time they didn't."

When money has not been the roadblock to earthquake
safety, apathy has. "It just seems that earthquake dangers
don't bother San Franciscans," Queiser said. "Some clown
against the bond issue made the argument that the odds
were eight to one against a child being in school at the time
of an earthquake so the money wasn't really needed." Public apathy toward the threats inherent in deficient schools
have not been a San Francisco exclusive. San Diego voters
failed three times within two years to appropriate the funds
necessary to strengthen or replace seventy-six pre-1933
school buildings serving fifteen thousand students. And
when the Board of Education sponsored meetings at various
unsafe schools to discuss methods and reasons for moving
students out of them, response from the parents whose children attended the unsafe schools was far from overwhelming. One meeting, held at a to-be-condemned junior high
school where fifteen hundred children attended classes,
drew only thirty-six parents. At another school meeting one
man argued that all the talk about earthquakes was "just a
big scare" tactic to wheedle more money out of the taxpayer. Parents at this second school voted not to have their

children transferred out of the unsafe building because the
move to new, strange schools would be too psychologically
traumatic for the children.

If a great earthquake strikes California during school
hours before the 1975 deadline, injuring or killing thousands
of children, the blame will not rest with the taxpayer alone.
As of 1971, 86 percent of the California school districts answering a survey by the State Department of Education reported that they still had unsafe buildings. All added that
they had undertaken a "recent" structural survey of the
buildings. However, according to the state board, some of
the surveys had been commissioned as far back as 1934. Of
305 districts in the state where pre-1933 school buildings
were still in use, almost 25 percent of the districts had, by
1971, adopted no plan for dealing with these hazardous
buildings. And of the 305 districts with pre-1933 buildings,
one-third had by 1971—four years after the legislature had
mandated action—not bothered to hold elections and had
made no plans to submit bond proposals to their voters.

If many school boards had done little or nothing to mitigate the dangers presented by their educational facilities,
others had done little or nothing to win the confidence of
the voters as bond issues were presented for approval.
Three Los Angeles bond issues—including one for $200 mil-
lion—were defeated partly because voters believed that
much of the money would be diverted to nonearthquake-re-
lated matters. San Francisco waged all-out campaigns to
win approval for two earthquake-safety bond issues—one
for $45 million and one for $56 million—both of which
failed. One campaign had included a dramatic demonstration of the potential effects of an earthquake on the city's
unsafe school buildings. A classroom identical to one in a
pre-1933 school was populated with mannequins and subjected to severe shaking similar to that induced by earthquake forces. Walls and ceilings tumbled down, giving tele-

vision stations and newspapers vivid pictures of severed "heads" and mangled "bodies." The voters, however, were far more impressed with charges from antibond forces that the money would be used, not to earthquakeproof schools, but to institute various school-modernization schemes unrelated to the protection of children.

Later, school officials admitted the charges were true and that only $28 million would have been necessary to meet the legislature's school-safety requirements. "We thought that it would make sense and save money in the long run if, as long as we had the schools torn open to make structural repairs, we also had them modernized to make them good educational facilities," Queiser explains half-heartedly. "The voters obviously didn't agree."

"Voters have come to distrust school officials," one State Department of Education official summarizes. "They have no faith that the boards will use the money for what they say they will, and maybe they are right. They have just had too many experiences with boards turning around and using the money somewhere else."

Public apathy and hostility, combined with official ineptitude, have left a dark cloud over California's schoolchildren. By 1971, of 123 bond elections held in California, only 51 had been approved by the voters. In 1968, there were more than 2000 unsafe school buildings in use throughout the state. By the end of 1970, the number had dropped only slightly to 1800. By 1972, the number had fallen to 1600 only because some Los Angeles–area school buildings damaged by the 1971 San Fernando earthquake had not been reopened.

Although the taxpayers and the various boards of education like to vest themselves in martyr's clothing when the question of earthquake safety in schools is discussed, the ultimate burden when bond issues are defeated falls on minority communities that occupy the older sections of the cities, precisely the areas where most of the pre-1933 school buildings still stand.

After the defeat of the third Los Angeles earthquake bond, for example, school officials decided that the minority students who would be displaced by the closing of unsafe schools would have to be crowded into double sessions in the handful of safe buildings available in the inner-city communities or in portable classrooms admittedly inadequate and substandard as educational facilities. The only other alternative was to bus the children to the more than two hundred vacant classrooms available in the newer (and overwhelmingly white) San Fernando Valley schools. In an attempt to ease some of the impact on the inner-city community, the board decided to let parents of the affected children choose among the three unpalatable alternatives. About 24 percent of the parents asked to have their children bussed to the San Fernando Valley. The rest chose to spare their children the long trip to the valley and resigned themselves to having the children attend double-session schools.

Even where voters have approved the sale of bonds to strengthen or replace pre-1933 buildings, the minority communities have had to struggle to force officials to spend appropriate portions of the newly received funds to replace the structurally substandard schools in their communities. In 1967 San Bernardino voters passed a substantial bond issue necessary to meet the specifications of the state's school-safety laws. But by 1971, with construction of new schools in white areas already well under way, the Board of Education still had not begun any new school construction in the city's Mexican-American section, even though three schools were shut down completely. The board also tried to convince the community that some schools in the area should be rebuilt or strengthened only in part because some of the campuses had "safe" post-1933 facilities. These so-called safe post-1933 facilities, the Board of Education con veniently tried to forget, were the educationally second-rate, portable classrooms used to relieve classroom shortages. Only when the community protested and forced the board to discuss the matter did officials relent and commit themselves to building entirely new schools in the Mexican-American community and to replacing some of the portable classrooms with permanent structures.

As the 1975 deadline for closing unsafe schools draws nearer, school districts that have been unable to raise the necessary funds to replace to-be-demolished schools have hoped—so far in vain—for help from other quarters. A sliver of light shone through the darkness when the California State Supreme Court struck down the state's requirement that school bond issues be approved by two-thirds of the electorate. (State Board of Education officials estimated that if only 51 percent of the voters were needed to approve a bond issue, 75 percent of the school bond proposals presented to the public in previous years would have passed.) The hope, however, was short-lived. On appeal from the state, the United States Supreme Court reversed the decision, allowing the two-thirds requirement to stand.

When Wilson Riles, state superintendent of public instruction, asked the State Board of Education—a conservative body dominated by men appointed by Governor Ronald Reagan—to back him in a campaign to have the two-thirds requirement repealed through a popular referendum, the board refused. Nor has Sacramento itself seemed disposed to bail out school districts with direct infusions of state cash. In its budget unveiled in early 1972, the Reagan administration included only thirty million dollars to be distributed to the state's school districts to help them meet state-imposed school-safety requirements. The legislature too has kept a tight fist around state funds.

The concern over earthquake hazards presented by the state's old buildings, public and private, builds up to and reaches a climax immediately after an earthquake. Private citizens, professional groups, and politicians, all of whom are suddenly aghast at the destruction and damage caused to old buildings, begin to clamor that "something must be done." Late in 1971, for example, the Los Angeles Earthquake Commission urgently suggested that the tens of thousands of unsafe buildings—variously estimated to number between twenty and forty thousand—in which more than three-quarters of a million persons work and live in the Los Angeles metropolitan area either be demolished or be brought up to earthquake-resistant standards by 1980.

But as earnest and well-meaning as the commission's recommendations were, if previous experience is any guide, they will never be acted upon. To be sure, public officials in Los Angeles and elsewhere have ample reserves of power, given them by building laws and court decisions, to implement the recommendations made by various committees, commissions, and building experts. Many cities have adopted model Uniform Building Code provisions that call, in very general terms, for some strengthening of hazardous buildings. Some cities, for example, have adopted Section 203a of the 1967 Uniform Building Code, which declares that "all buildings or structures which are structurally unsafe . . . or otherwise dangerous to human life . . . by reason of obsolescence . . . are . . . unsafe buildings. All such unsafe buildings are hereby declared to be public nuisances and shall be abated by repair, rehabilitation, demolition or removal. . . ." Other cities have adopted another model Uniform Building Code provision that requires a building's owner to undertake some structural strengthening if and when he makes additions to the building or starts other necessary repairs.

The judicial sanctions for official action against old buildings came as the result of a long battle between Bakersfield city officials and the stubborn owner of an old, worn-out eight-story hotel gracing the city's center.

In the mid 1950s, Bakersfield city officials inspected the Hotel Padre and decided that the antiquated hotel was a dangerous firetrap. The building's interior stairways were unenclosed, leaving an open shaft, running from the second floor to the roof, a convenient conduit through which fire and smoke could race from floor to floor. The hotel's elevator shafts were also improperly closed off. Many shafts and ducts throughout the hotel contained combustible materials and could not be closed off in case of fire. The boiler room, fire officials found, was not separated from the rest of the building by fire-resistant materials. Exit signs were small and badly lit. Fire escapes were badly constructed. Transoms over sleeping-room doors were used as return routes for the hotel's air-conditioning system. They would also serve as prime channels through which smoke could spread from room to room during a fire, especially in summer, when they were often open.

Fire officials, at first far from militant, tried to cajole the hotel's owner, one Milton Miller, into taking the necessary steps to make the building safer for its occupants. Miller, in a series of conferences with city officials, pleaded financial hardship and claimed he could not afford to make the changes—the installation of a sprinkler system, modification of the fire-escape network, sealing off of fire- and smoke-conducting ducts—suggested by fire officials. In 1959, after the city adopted the Uniform Building Code, one fire captain suggested to Miller that he make some changes to demonstrate his good faith. Miller responded in 1960 by shoring up one single fire escape.

By August, 1960, the city's patience had grown exceedingly thin and Miller was told that he had forty-eight hours in which to start making additional fire-prevention corrections on his firetrap. When Miller ignored these warnings, the City Council passed a special resolution demanding that Miller install a sprinkler system in the basement and first floor of the building within six months and that he modify successive floors until, at the end of twelve years, he had covered the entire hotel with the fire-fighting system. Miller's only response to the City Council resolution, the State Supreme Court was to note in its decision against the hotel owner, "was to erect what he described as an 'Alamo-Tombstone' sign on the building to herald his defiance of the city council." The city, at the end of its tether, filed suit to force Miller to adhere to its newly adopted code.

The courts (the suit went through a series of appeals) were asked to resolve one basic question: was it constitutional for a city to apply standards of safety incorporated in a recently adopted code to buildings constructed before the code had been embraced? The city of Bakersfield, joined in its supplication to the courts by some other cities, argued that it should have the right to force owners of old buildings to raze them or to bring them up to modern-day standards. Miller argued that the city did not, and should not, have such a right.

The State Supreme Court showed little sympathy for Miller's arguments. Even if a building had been constructed in accordance with all existing statutes when it was built, the high court ruled, the building was not necessarily immune from subsequent control meant to diminish its potential threat as a public hazard. "The city does not seek to impose punitive sanctions for the methods of construction in 1929," the court ruled, "but to eliminate a presently existing danger to the public. It would be unreasonable limitation on the powers of the city to require that this danger be tolerated ad infinitum merely because the hotel did not violate the statutes in effect when it was constructed thirty-six years ago."

The code provisions and the judicial sanctions, however, have gathered dust. Widespread lethargy, shortages of funds and manpower, fears of political repercussions have served, singly or in combination, to stifle effective abatement of hazards posed by old buildings.

The San Bernardino Building Department, for example, has a back door opening onto a courtyard enclosed on all sides by a host of buildings. If city officials are asked if they have a program to require the removal or renovation of old buildings, one man will open the back door. "If we did," he sighs, making a sweeping gesture around the courtyard, "we would have to remove that building and that one and that one. So what can we do?" City officials in San Francisco, where an ordinance requiring the removal of parapets and other appendages from old buildings has been on the books for more than five years, have yet to appropriate the money necessary to enforce the law.*

Even cities that take some steps to cope with their hazardous buildings eventually falter, usually hampered by rapidly diminishing interest and continual struggles over money.

After the 1969 earthquake, Santa Rosa officials decided they would try to rid the city, once and for all, of the scores of old and unsafe buildings (many of which had been rebuilt immediately after the 1906 earthquake) crowding the city's central area. The City Council authorized the formation of a committee, headed by John Brown, to study the problem and to make recommendations. Brown's committee, representing a cross section of the community, recommended that all buildings (except schools and single-family residences) built before 1957, the year the city first started enforcing its building codes, be inspected by qualified engineers and city officials.

* "In San Francisco they say they haven't got the money to enforce the parapet law," John Brown, a Santa Rosa structural engineer, says. "They have enough money for a Columbus Day parade every year, though."

Once buildings had been evaluated, the committee recommended, they were to be acted upon according to three hard-and-fast rules: buildings that had been judged to be immediately dangerous either had to be strengthened or had to be demolished within one year; buildings that were a remote danger, either because they did not accommodate many people or because they were seldom used, had to be destroyed or renovated within five years; buildings that had been fairly well constructed in the first place and could be saved with a minimum of effort could be brought up to approved safety standards over a period of ten years.

For all the urgency felt in 1969, full enforcement of the committee's recommendations was still not under way thirty months after the earthquake. Some old buildings, it is true, did come down when the city received some urban-renewal funds after the earthquake. However, scores of old buildings escaped the urban-renewal bulldozer. And, as 1972 began to wane, it seemed highly unlikely that city officials would ever deal firmly with Santa Rosa's remaining hazardous buildings. The city's Building Department, already hard pressed for time and manpower to keep up with the demands posed by new construction, was still waiting for the City Council to act on the department's request for money to add two engineers and three inspectors to its staff, additions that would help the department begin some appraisals of old buildings but would still leave it too shorthanded to undertake a vigorous attack on the problem. "Under optimal conditions," Brown says in disgust, "the program could have been completed in three or four years. But the program would cost the city and the property owners money, and the memory of 1969 is fading fast. The way things stand now, it will be a close race between the sun dying and Santa Rosa finally becoming earthquake-resistant."

Perhaps the only city to have undertaken—and to have followed through to a respectable degree—an abatement program aimed at old buildings is Los Angeles. But even here the exigencies of urban finance have affected the program's success.

Los Angeles began its program to "harden" hazardous buildings against the ravages of earthquakes in 1948, fifteen years after the Long Beach earthquake had demonstrated the vulnerability of Los Angeles's older buildings. "After that earthquake," Robert C. Adolphe, chief of the Los Angeles Conservation Bureau, says, "it would have been economically impossible to tear down every building that was not sound. It would have been worse than the earthquake. So we decided to do the next best thing. We decided to go after the buildings where we could save some lives."

A substantial part of the abatement program called for the identification and removal of overhanging appendages and parapets. These building appointments, which architects had considered smart additions to their designs, could easily be shaken loose by earthquakes and hurled to pavements crowded with pedestrians. By 1971, the city had managed to have parapets and appendages removed from almost seventeen thousand buildings. However, parapets and appendages on almost four thousand other buildings had still not succumbed to the city's efforts by 1971.

While the Conservation Bureau has committed itself to inspect every residential building in Los Angeles by 1983—with special emphasis on older buildings in the city's disadvantaged areas—no comparable goal has been set to investigate some 350,000 commercial buildings. Forced by lack of manpower and money to choose between residential and commercial buildings, the city decided to allocate its scarce resources to protecting people in their homes. As a result, city inspectors have been limited to investigating only those commercial buildings referred by the fire or police departments, by private individuals, or by elected officials prodded by constituents angry over problems in their buildings.

"It is apparent," Karl Steinbrugge says, "that *legal tools* are available to deal with buildings presenting an earthquake collapse hazard. The *economic* consequences of literal enforcement could, of course, cause political repercussions. As a result, retroactive ordinances are usually applied leniently."

The prime case study of successful political pressure to bring about a lenient interpretation of laws aimed at hazardous buildings came in Long Beach, where, in 1966, Ed O'Connor, director of the Long Beach Department of Building and Safety, had decided to wage a no-nonsense war on the city's older structures.

Under the Long Beach building code, O'Connor had had the right to conduct a hazard-abatement campaign since the late 1950s. That right, however, had been clouded as long as the Miller case had been before the courts. But when the State Supreme Court ruled against Miller, in 1966 O'Connor undertook, with some relish, his antihazardous building campaign. By May 31, 1969, his department had sent out 117 letters of outright condemnation and 149 letters requesting that owners voluntarily demolish or repair their earthquake-damage-prone buildings.

O'Connor's zeal, however, soon ran afoul of Long Beach property owners, who united to lobby and pressure the City Council to weaken the Building Department's powers. If O'Connor were allowed to continue in his determination to rid Long Beach of earthquake-hazardous buildings, the property owners screamed, more than three thousand buildings—60 percent of the downtown Long Beach area— would be affected. Under O'Connor, the Building Department, the owners complained, had "arbitrarily embarked upon a program of bringing all buildings up to what they consider would make them impervious to damage by earthquakes. . . ." Furthermore, the owners said, the department had "appreciably accelerated inspection activity in all

other buildings they purport come within their general jurisdiction. Their attitude of enforcement has become unreasonable because items requiring corrective attention have
increased in number, and costs to comply are prohibitive.
Anyone unable to comply runs the risk of losing their property, their life savings and their future income."

"A great number of structural engineers from their ivory
towers and their laboratories feel that there is no question
about it, we have to crank up the bulldozers and build a
shining new City of Oz in Long Beach," Phil E. Poppler,
chairman of the Long Beach property owners' legal committee, complained to the City Council. "Well, we all know it
can't be done. The thing we have forgotten is where is the
Gaza Strip, where are these displaced persons going to be
housed and how are they going to be housed. How is a con-
dominium owner or tenant, one of our poor and elderly senior citizens or minority persons, where are they going to find
housing at fifty or sixty-five dollars per month within a pen-
sion budget based on Social Security income. Are we just
going to put them out on an ice floe like the Eskimos do
with their old women and their old men, send them out to
sea?"

The property owners' concern for the minorities, the elderly, and the poor was touching, if not somewhat sudden, inconsistent, exceedingly self-serving, and misleading. Other
speakers representing the association before the council
begged the councilmen to stay the Building Department's
corrective and razing orders because within a few years the
downtown area would be completely refurbished through
urban-renewal programs. Then, property owners said, the
city would be rid of its hazards and they would have a
chance to profit on their investments. No one, of course,
talked about *not* demolishing their buildings under urban
renewal because those poor, old, minority people, lucky to
find cheap accommodations in hazardous buildings, would

then be displaced by glass and aluminum office buildings and high-priced apartment buildings. Furthermore, at times, the property owners carried on as if demolition of their buildings had been the only alternative presented to them. In reality, O'Connor told the council in rebuttal, his department had been giving the owners ample opportunities to repair their property. In fact, several owners, O'Connor said, had chosen to strengthen their buildings, making them more resistant to earthquakes. The recalcitrant owners simply did not want to spend the money necessary to protect those to whom they rented space.

To a considerable degree, the property owners managed to blunt the directness and effectiveness of O'Connor's approach. Hoping to arrive at some compromise, the City Council spent ten thousand dollars to hire a private consultant to study Long Beach's hazardous-building problems.

The consultant's report was long and detailed, encompassing an impressive array of suggestions (including recommendations that a seismic-risk map of the city be done) city officials might follow to ease the hazards presented by old buildings. Also included in the report was a complicated formula—one of the first efforts to put earthquake-hazard analysis on an objective basis, some experts felt—to determine the extent of the dangers presented to people by an old building coming to the attention of city officials. Part of the formula, now a part of the Long Beach city building code, reads:

The average human exposure [to earthquake danger in an old building] shall be computed by multiplying the average number of persons exposed by the average number of hours they are exposed during some selected period of computation and dividing it by the number of hours in the period of computation selected. The "persons exposed" shall include those persons who are within the structure during the period of computation as well as those persons who are outside the structure, but so located with respect to it as to be reasonably endangered should it suffer a major structural failure due to earthquake occurring while they are so located.

The "period of computation" shall be that period not less than one complete day, which is sufficient to include one full cycle of any reasonably cyclical variation in the number of persons exposed to danger should the structure experience a major structural failure due to earthquake.

For example, if the structure is an office building in which twenty people on the average work an average of eight hours a day, five days a week, fifty weeks a year, and an average of one hundred twenty people walk back and forth directly in front of the building every day of the year with an average transit time of thirty seconds each, the "period of computation" is one week. During that week, persons inside the building are each exposed for an average of forty hours. Thus, these are eight hundred person-hours of exposure per week registered by people inside. On the outside, one hundred and twenty persons register an average of one person-hour per day, or seven person-hours per week. The total of eight hundred seven person-hours per week, divided by one hundred and sixty-eight hours per week, yields an Average Human Exposure of slightly less than five persons. The hazard, then, is equivalent to that which would be presented if five people stayed in the structure twenty-five hours a day and no one walked back and forth outside.

The formula was elaborately elegant. It also proved to be the loophole the property owners had been waiting for.

Primarily, the formula made it all too easy to view the danger to 140 very real persons who might be caught at high noon in a sixty-five-year-old building during an earthquake as danger to a handful of cipherlike figures exposed to the tremor at four o'clock on a Sunday morning. Anyone using the formula to determine the levels of hazard that should be tolerated in Long Beach can talk in terms of six "persons exposed" or ten "persons exposed" in an old building. It is not necessary, in other words, to carry on unsavory debates whether old buildings should be allowed to kill one hundred or two hundred men, women, or children. But more important, the formula, combined with those ordinance sections outlining actual methods for reducing a building's dangers, makes it all too easy for the property owner to participate in the actuarial calisthenics and to avoid making substantive improvements to make his building safer. To be sure, he could, following orders from an official like O'Connor, undertake conventional steps to abate the hazards presented by his building. He could abandon it, demolish it, or proceed with conventional repairs to protect those who would be in his building during an earthquake. But the new ordinances also give him the choice of lowering the theoretical number of people exposed by making some nonstructural changes in his building. For example, calculations undertaken when his building comes to the Building Department's attention may show that the equivalent of ten persons are exposed to danger in his eight-story department store during an arbitrary twenty-five-hour period. The owner, on appealing the department's repair orders against his building, is allowed by the new laws to diminish the number of "persons exposed" by diminishing the values of some of the ingredients used in the formula. He could, for example, seal off two floors in the building and circumscribe the number of hours the building is open to the public. In other words, a dangerous department store could be made safer, not by shoring up its deficient walls, but by roping off floors rarely used and moving the store's closing time back from 10:00 P.M. to 8:00 P.M. According to the formula, the number of "persons exposed" to danger would be dramatically cut. Once the new calculations are finished, there is a theoretical increase in earthquake safety. But in real life, there would be little or no difference. Whatever the paper choplogic might show, hundreds of persons would still be subject to death and injury if they were caught in the building at an inopportune time. Similarly, the owner of an unsafe theater could cut in half the number of theoretical "persons exposed" by cutting performances or by roping off his balcony. The formula would reflect a diminished danger. But again, the abracadabra would be of little use to those people in the audience, should an earthquake strike on a Saturday evening during a John Wayne double feature.

O'Connor, of course, is disgusted with the results of the consultant's work. "The adoption of new ordinances to follow the consultant's recommendations meant that we had to start all over again with our notices of condemnation and the appeals proceedings," O'Connor says. "So, we have lost time there. But even when we catch up with the new ordinances, if we ever have a long-lasting earthquake, it would still be a danger to life and limb and an economic catastrophe as well.

"The simpler you keep the solution to the problem, the better the chances of resolving it in a reasonable manner.

"The loss of one life should not be tolerated in any of those obsolete buildings. They weren't good when they were put up in the first place and they sure as hell are not like whiskey. They don't get better with age. The consultant gave us a thick report and we got a complicated ordinance out of it. But my position is, and always has been, those buildings ain't no damn good. Fix them up or let's tear them down."

Chapter Seven

Every year, California builders, working mightily to keep pace with the state's growing and spreading population, begin ten billion dollars' worth of construction. Virtually all of it—homes, apartment buildings, office complexes, electrical power plants, superhighways—is destined to suffer more than its share of destruction. Much of it will kill more people than necessary. California construction is no match for earthquakes because the state's building codes, the legal mechanisms through which local governments theoretically try to guarantee engineering and design safety, are inadequate. The vast majority of engineers responsible for assorted projects have neither the time, the expertise, nor the financial freedom to make their projects truly earthquake-resistant. California's construction workmanship, geared to rush schedules and minimal financial outlays, is often slipshod. Inspections meant to supervise building practices are severely hampered by a shortage of funds and properly trained personnel.

Proof that California buildings are no match for earthquakes has come in tremors in California and in other seismic areas where building practices are patterned after those followed in California. "The fact that all problems have not been solved is clearly evident from the extensive damage to many buildings in Anchorage during the 1964 Alaskan earthquake," Karl Steinbrugge wrote in *Earthquake Hazard*. "Most of the damaged buildings were designed to be earthquake resistive in some degree, most buildings were built under construction standards common to many parts of the United States. Unfortunately, similar circumstances are found in other cities where a large earthquake can cause similar damage. In the next great earthquake, some Bay area cities quite possibly will also witness the collapse of modern buildings, which probably had their counterparts in Anchorage in 1964."

In Caracas in 1967, modern buildings, constructed according to provisions of codes based on the most modern of California's laws and designed by recognized engineers, suffered extensive damage. In Santa Rosa in 1969, new buildings, barely finished before a mild earthquake struck the area, were hard hit by the tremor. Extensive damage to brand-new county-owned buildings, a grand jury investigation concluded, came about because the buildings met only the barest of standards set by the 1964 Uniform Building Code, adopted by Santa Rosa, in itself a minimal law. "The damage to earthquake resistive buildings in Santa Rosa was more than expected by many engineers for a magnitude five to six earthquake," a U.S. Department of Commerce report by Karl Steinbrugge, William Cloud, and Nina Scott, said. "Thus a fresh review of some American building code provisions appears to be in order."

Although a few cities write and amend their own building codes, many jurisdictions adopt model codes (including periodic, recommended revisions and amendments) written by one of a handful of organizations composed of building officials representing cities and towns in various states. These organizations, including the International Conference of Building Officials (ICBO), which writes model codes for California and some western and midwestern states, really function only as funnels. The codes they channel to cities are the products of recommendations "poured" into the building-official organizations by various, specialized groups.

From time to time, for example, building officials from one county, any one of a number of materials manufacturers, academicians from Berkeley or Caltech, or professional groups such as the Structural Engineers Association (SEA) will suggest a code revision or amendment to ICBO. The recommendation, after a review by ICBO staff technicians, is referred to an appropriate ICBO committee, where the recommendation is subject to public hearings and further review. If the committee approves a recommended change or addition to the code, the recommendation is then brought before a triannual general meeting, where only building officials, the ones who enforce the building code, are allowed to vote on the measure. Of course, if a code change is rejected by a committee, the champions of the change can still bring it to the floor of the general meeting and attempt to persuade those in attendance to adopt their recommendation despite the committee's negative evaluation. All changes approved by the general meeting, however, are in themselves useless until they are approved by individual cities, towns, and counties for use within their jurisdictions. Only then do the codes and revisions or amendments assume the power of law. Adoption of new code specifications is not always automatic. Some cities never adopt building codes. Others adopt a code and then neglect to keep it up to date. The city of Long Beach, for example, operated under the same building code from 1958 to 1971, even though the model Uniform Building Code drafted by the ICBO had been changed several times in the interim.

In theory, the code-writing system should work well. There are opportunities to draw on the experience and knowledge of a diverse group of experts, theoreticians and practitioners alike. Ample checks and balances seem to be provided by staff reviews, committee hearings, general meetings, and channels of appeal.

The building codes, however, are marred by serious deficiencies, not the least of which is their resounding silence on some crucial architectural aspects of construction. Very often, for example, engineers and architects begin to use new materials in buildings, slowly expanding their uses over the years. In studying Santa Rosa buildings damaged by the 1969 earthquake, for example, Steinbrugge, Cloud, and Scott noted that new materials had been a part of many of the more modern buildings. Sprayed on fireproofing replacing poured-in-place concrete fireproofing had become common. Glass and metal skins, lithe and light, had replaced the more solid brick and concrete walls that had been part of buildings in earlier years. The net effect of the new materials, the trio said, "has been to substantially reduce . . . the resistance of buildings." The code writers, while making a studied show of trying to bolster earthquake safety by requiring measures that would increase building strengths, have never tried to control the role these new materials play in building—directly or indirectly—or to outline their effects on the sturdiness of a building.

Among the architectural constituents of construction ignored by the codes have been the interior designs of buildings. A few individual jurisdictions have independently modified their codes to regulate architectural elements in construction. They require, for example, that window frames in new buildings be designed so that the glass they contain does not shatter when the frames are deformed by an earthquake. Some jurisdictions also require light fixtures to be designed and hung so that they will not fall during a tremor. These few regulations, however, are the exceptions and not the rule. The result has been excessive property damage and unnecessary threats to life during earthquakes.

For example, many buildings that escaped severe structural damage during the San Fernando earthquake suffered extensive architectural damage. Plaster partitions fractured; ceilings cracked and in some cases toppled to the floor. Buildings were severely damaged because heavy mechanical and electrical equipment, essential parts of a building's interior finish, had bounced around during the quake. Air-conditioning units and other heavy equipment also fell off their mountings. "Much of this damage," a report by Caltech said, "could have been avoided by giving attention to earthquake effects when the finish and equipment were designed. . . . This improvement in resistance could have been achieved with little extra cost. There was little window breakage in the high rise buildings, which shows that architectural damage can indeed be controlled." Adds Dr. James Slosson, "The modern design of the new high rise buildings makes it extremely unlikely that they would collapse in an earthquake of large intensity. Structural engineering has accomplished great things. But the interior mechanics of these tall buildings are their Achilles' heels."

If unregulated architectural design has left buildings with architectural soft spots, one of the most crucial may be the elevators used in medium- and high-rise buildings. According to several studies, the February 9 earthquake caused elevators to fail in almost all of the tallest buildings in the downtown Los Angeles area. Just how many individual elevators were really affected has been difficult to establish, but according to surveys conducted by at least twelve elevator companies in the area, 100 elevators stopped functioning because their cables snarled. At least 174 elevators were put out of commission when their electric generators failed, and more than 600 elevators failed because their counterweights were knocked off their guide rails. In more than one hundred cases where elevator counterweights were derailed, they crashed against the elevator cabs, sometimes coming to rest on their roofs, sometimes crashing into the elevator's interior. According to Professor Samuel Aroni of UCLA, additional, hidden dangers lurk in the elevator mechanism's faulty response to tremors. In an earthquake, he says, "a counterweight could become fully detached from its rails, with the elevator remaining operative. Thus, before the damage could be discovered, an unaware person could use the elevator and cause a collision with the counterweight."

Widespread elevator failures, says J. M. Ayres, a consulting mechanical engineer, can mean more than loss of escape routes. "It is not practical to get people out of these big, tall buildings in emergencies, and the experts have concluded that they [the people] must have places of refuge inside where they will be safe from fire," Ayres said. "But the elevators have to work so that fire fighting and other emergency equipment can get up to the floors involved most seriously. That is why they must continue to function in these tall buildings, even where the occupants are protected by fire walls and other emergency devices." To compound the problems posed by disabled elevators, local building practices in many areas often allow stairs in some buildings to act as diagonal braces between floors. Staircases, however, are often weak, and the same earthquake forces that render elevators inoperative can buckle and topple stairs, cutting off still another escape route and still another avenue through which rescue operations can reach those trapped on upper floors of a building.

There is some evidence that codes should address themselves—at least in principle—to another aspect of architecture they have ignored: the stylistic designs given new modern buildings.

Architects and engineers know, for example, that one of the best earthquake-resistant designs is one that in effect ties a building together, giving it a fairly regular shape, and which plants it firmly in the ground. In such a building, all the parts of the structure are well supported and can act in concert to help absorb and dispel the onslaught of earthquake energy. Yet California builders all too often raise their inspired creations on slender pods, stilts, or narrow columns to instill a lighter-than-air feeling in the viewer's eyes. These various supports, often designed to minimal girth, though pleasing to behold, are of doubtful value during an intense earthquake. Furthermore, buildings are all too often constructed in various and assorted shapes—including T, U, and L formations in which the various wings of a building, rather than acting in unison during a tremor, crash and grind against each other until they have managed to destroy or damage themselves and the building. "Architects," says one engineer, "have just not helped matters by promoting styles that are not very good for earthquake resistance. They control the construction, and, if they get any flack from their engineers, they can always go out and get another man who doesn't raise objections." However, architects alone cannot be made to carry all the blame for squeezing questionable design practices into the voids left by the building codes. "For a lot of structural engineers," says one engineer in a large California architectural firm, "it's a matter of ego when architects come to them with a far-out design. Those engineers are always tempted to prove that they can make it earthquake-safe."

The architectural flights of fancy ignored by the code are most often seen in the designs of private homes. As a result, the single-family dwelling is not always the safe haven from earthquakes the experts would like to pretend it is.

The Kern County earthquake of 1952 was among the first to demonstrate that trends in modern home design can set the scene for potential earthquake disaster. "Many residences," Karl Steinbrugge and Don Moran, a consulting structural engineer, wrote after studying the 1952 earthquake's effects, "have continuous picture windows in addition to a double garage door opening. The lack of balanced resisting elements can cause damage due to twisting and cracking. Steep hillsides are now being covered with homes. One side of the residence may be one story while the other may be two or three stories. In summary, it is probable that the overall behavior of wood frame dwellings in future shocks may not be as good as it has been in past shocks."

Some would argue that Steinbrugge's and Moran's findings are long out of date, that modern home-construction techniques (such as the ones supposedly slated for Redwood Shores) are more than adequate to minimize property damage and danger to the inhabitants from earthquake forces. Such optimism, however, is hardly warranted, especially in the light of damage wrought on modern homes by the San Fernando earthquake.

Caltech researchers found that some of the San Fernando Valley's two-story homes had proven particularly vulnerable to the earthquake, especially two-story and split-level homes in which one or more bedrooms had been placed over the garage. In some instances, Caltech investigators found, the garage walls in the valley homes had failed, and overhead bedrooms had crashed to the ground. Many split-level homes were damaged, the Los Angeles County Earthquake Commission said, "when unbraced cripple walls were used to support interior walls, when large openings were designed and constructed resulting in lack of braced walls, or when tops of walls were inadequately interconnected."

After the earthquake, students from UCLA's School of Architecture and Urban Planning, researching house-building practices in the San Fernando Valley, found that many homes could have been potential deathtraps. In house after house, the student researchers found inadequate or non-existent bracing in such critical areas as the family room, the kitchen, and the living room. In many of these oft-used rooms, standard walls, which should have included proper bracing, had been replaced by long glass doors or window spans. The expanses of glass deprived the houses of adequate support. Had they shattered at a time of day when the room would have been in use, they would have posed an additional danger to the family.

Many two-story homes in the valley had badly supported stairs that failed during the earthquake, trapping the family on the upstairs level. In many homes, freestanding, two-story fireplaces or two-story expanses of glass stood next to the main stairs. In at least one case, a freestanding fireplace collapsed into a heap of bricks, effectively blocking the route from the stairs to the front door. Exit routes free of huge fireplaces or fancy glassworks were in the shadow of lamps dangling from long, heavy chains. Outside the homes, balconies or sloping roofs, covered with heavy tiles, hovered over the doors.

While most California cities and towns have ignored this latest evidence damning inadequate architectural control of home construction, at least Los Angeles seems to have learned its lesson. After the earthquake, the city amended its building code to require future homes to have additional bracing in foundation stud walls, steel bracing in chimneys, anchors to hold chimneys and water heaters to the frame of the house, and connectors to hold veneer surfaces to wooden studs in the frame.

The effectiveness of the building code in preventing earthquake hazards is compromised not by sins of omission alone, but by extensive sins of commission as well. The code-writing process, for all its external appearances of rationality, is marked by inter- and intra-professional squabbling, strident and unproductive competition among materials industries, and assorted pressures brought to bear on the writers of the code. The entire process, in fact, is more of a testament to the give-and-take of back-room politics than it is to an intelligent approach to earthquake safety.

The Structural Engineers Association, for example, wields great power in the drafting of codes by originating code recommendations itself and by advising the ICBO on code changes recommended by other groups. Although structural engineers are, as one professor of engineering says, "gold-plated nuts on the subject of earthquake safety," their participation in the code-writing process has not necessarily guaranteed the evolution of a code suited to protect the public.

The structural engineers who have the greatest influence on proposed code changes are those who either have or take the time to work on the SEA committees charged with supervising building-code changes or who can serve on the Board of Directors, the body that puts the final seal of approval on recommendations that go out under the SEA's name. While those who serve on these various committees are dedicated and able men, they do not represent the full range of opinion or expertise within the rank and file of the association. And since the membership is not polled when a code recommendation is considered, the opinion, in essence, reflects the thoughts and experiences of only a handful of men.

Furthermore, the California Structural Engineers Association is divided into northern, central, southern, and San Diego chapters, each with its own code committee and board of directors. On more than one occasion, Los Angeles and San Francisco code committees have come to different conclusions on a suggested or needed code change, and the two chapters have found themselves at loggerheads. The differences occur because the northern structural engineers think themselves far more experienced because they had the state's first great earthquake in an urban area, while the southerners think they have the greater sophistication because they implemented the first earthquake safety codes in the state. To preserve organizational unity and to make possible a much cherished uniformity in building practices, the two sides often have to negotiate over recommended changes that have elicited diverse opinions in the two parts of the state. "It is no different than in politics," one leading structural engineer says. "In some of these things you have to go in the back door and work things out." Obviously, a decision based on political astuteness or a political give-and-take is not always compatible with earthquake safety.

Finally, because the structural engineers are the recognized elite of the engineering profession (it takes years of additional study and practice, not to mention special tests, to gain accreditation as a structural engineer), they often tend to regard practitioners of other engineering specialties with a touch of condescension. As a result, other engineers interested in earthquake safety, men and women with their own ideas about new approaches to the problem, sometimes have to fight their way into the code-writing process. "When it comes down to writing the code," Douglas Moran says, "there is a lot of stratification. The structural engineers consider themselves the top. So when the soils engineers sat down and wrote a recommended chapter for the Uniform Building Code, the structural engineers were offended and tried for a number of years to kill all the changes recommended by the soils engineers. The chapter the soils engineers wanted was finally adopted, but only after the soils engineers formed a committee that included some structural engineers."

Building codes, especially those sections meant to ensure construction of earthquake-resistant structures, are written with several considerations in mind. Their "philosophical" objective is to protect lives by eliciting the construction of buildings that would suffer damage but would not collapse with people still inside or on top of people passing by. The codes' practical objectives are to delineate—in complicated mathematical formulations—the earthquake forces that a building should be designed to resist, and to define the earthquake-resistant qualities construction materials must have if they are to be approved for use.

The definition and understanding of earthquake forces and the analysis of the effects of forces on structures and on the ground on which these structures stand have been left to a small, financially undernourished group of university and government researchers. The result has been a considerable lag in research. Even the latest codes, adopted by the most progressive cities, require buildings to withstand forces calculated under crude circumstances more than thirty years ago.

For example, current earthquake codes require that a building with rigid walls be capable of resisting ground accelerations of 13 percent. That is, the building must be designed to withstand, without suffering structural damage, accelerations or forces equal to 13 percent of the building's weight. Yet engineers have known for several years that forces actually released by earthquakes can and have been higher than that figure, an understanding confirmed by measurements of the San Fernando earthquake. According to this latest information, buildings in some parts of Los Angeles were subject to forces as high as 23 percent of their gross weight. In the areas closest to the earthquake, the ground accelerations were even more intense. Olive View Hospital, it has been estimated, was subject to earthquake forces four times greater than those local codes had outlined. In effect, then, a code that requires buildings to resist ground accelerations of only 13 percent is a minimal code.

While the research into earthquake forces has been left to fund-strapped theoreticians who only recently have begun to receive the necessary numbers of sensitive instruments they need to refine their measurements, the research into the performance of building materials under earthquake strain has been undertaken by well-endowed private companies and industrial groups eager to market new products or anxious to find new uses for older, established products.

The lure of profit has led the various materials industries to make some contributions to earthquake safety. But all too often, the codes' writers, with little or no money to carry out independent tests to confirm all of the data presented by industry technicians, must accept the claims made by those who champion a particular construction material. As a result, both the SEA and the ICBO, despite hot denials, have been cornered into sanctioning the use of established materials in doubtful ways as well as endorsing the incorporation of new, unproven materials in newer projects.

In the early and mid-1960s, for example, the Structural Engineers Association decided that the trend toward highrise construction in major California cities called for a reevaluation of building practices. These new buildings, it came to be accepted, had to have frames that could withstand extreme forces without twisting permanently out of shape. Such frames, called ductile frames, would not necessarily save property, but they would save lives. They would best be made, SEA decided, of structural steel.

The Portland Cement Association, the nation's leading spokesman for the concrete industry, took exception to the SEA decision. With a boom in high-rise construction clearly ahead as Los Angeles, San Francisco, and other cities expanded upward instead of outward, any decision that would exclude reinforced concrete from use in the frames of the new high-rise buildings would cost the concrete industry hundreds of millions of dollars.

Faced by the intense crescendo of protests from the Portland group, the SEA (and the ICBO) deferred a final decision. If the concrete manufacturers could demonstrate that reinforced concrete could be made to incorporate ductile qualities similar to those of steel, the engineering group said, it could be persuaded to ease its stand against materials other than steel. Given sufficient proof, SEA added, it would recommend that new codes should require high-rise buildings to have frames of steel or any material that *acted like steel.* As a result of this concession, the concrete industry spent thousands of dollars in attempts to make reinforced concrete ductile and to prove it worthy of use in high buildings.

When it believed it had developed a ductile reinforced concrete, the Portland Cement Association spent an almost equal amount of energy and time to convince the ICBO and the structural engineers that its success was real. Much of this intense campaign, however, was also dedicated to convince the Structural Engineers Association and the ICBO that they should water down some of their requirements for ductile materials. Specifically, Portland wanted the codes to set lower limits on the forces the ductile frames would have to resist than some members of the SEA considered wise. To meet lower limits of resistance, the concrete could be combined with fewer reinforcing steel rods, thereby making the use of reinforced concrete cheaper and more competitive with structural steel.

The Structural Engineers Association finally accepted the industry's arguments that reinforced concrete could be used in high-rise building frames—but not before southern and northern California faced off in one of those back-room meetings. The northern engineers were, for a time, strongly opposed to the liberalization of code requirements proposed for the new high rises. They could see nothing advantageous in the use of reinforced-concrete frames for the towering buildings slated for San Francisco's horizons. "Our local seismology committee," one northern structural engineer complained bitterly, "and our local board of directors, in order to prevent a split-up of our state association, had to agree to a weakening of our earthquake-code requirements because of the extreme pressure from certain materials producers. . . ." Once the SEA capitulated, the ICBO accepted the use of reinforced-concrete frames. Major cities, where the Portland Cement Association had lobbied assiduously while waiting for the SEA and ICBO to make up their minds, also came to accept the reinforced-concrete frames.

Even as the new codes were being written, sanctioning the use of reinforced concrete in high-rise frames, the engineering dissenters warned that disaster was being courted. "Our failures [in the next earthquake]," one engineer warned, "will not merely be failures of six-story-high buildings of lift-slab construction. They will be failures of ten-story, twenty-story, or higher buildings of very recent vintage and supposedly designed to meet our own earthquake-code provisions."

Reinforced concrete can be a worthwhile construction material, especially if used under tightly controlled circumstances by highly knowledgeable practitioners. But the continuing opposition to the use of reinforced-concrete frames in high rises was based on cumulative experience, ranging from Anchorage in 1964 to San Fernando in 1971, that demonstrated that concrete is far too easy to abuse. Many engineers are sloppy in their attention to the finer nuances in designing with reinforced concrete, often ignoring details essential to making a structure earthquake-resistant. Experience has also shown that even if the engineer pays attention to detail, on-site workers often do not.

Reinforced concrete holds special potential for abuse because pillars, slabs, and columns are poured at the site of

construction, whether they are to fit on the second floor of a
three-story building or are made to be hoisted for placement
hundreds of feet above the ground. Concrete, for example,
for lift-slab construction is poured in sections whose sizes
are determined by the amount of finished material that can
be used in one day. In order to properly bind one section of
concrete to another, the border between the two slabs
(called a construction joint) should be cleaned by sand blasts
or with a chipping hammer. If the slab edges coming together are not carefully cleaned, they become covered with
an unstable material that froths to the top of the fresh concrete as it hardens. The material, known as laitance, inter-
feres with proper binding between two blocks of concrete,
severely weakening the ability of the wall or floor they compose to withstand earthquake forces. Studying the 1952
Kern County earthquake, Steinbrugge and Moran found
ample evidence of sloppy work on joints marking the reinforced-concrete buildings used at the time. Where the two
investigators found badly damaged buildings, they found
that sections of reinforced concrete had slipped past each
other at their borders.

Almost fifteen years later, the moderate 1967 earthquake
(6.5 on the Richter scale) in Caracas again pointed a shaky
finger at reinforced concrete's vulnerability. Caracas is a
fairly modern city. In the decade between 1957 and 1967,
almost one thousand high-rise buildings, many of them between ten and thirty stories high, soared into the skyline.
The buildings, in which builders nearly always had used reinforced concrete in the hope that it would be earthquake-
resistant, were constructed under code provisions based on
California's latest codes.

American researchers investigating the structural aspects
of collapsed and damaged buildings felt that the quality of
reinforced-concrete construction in Caracas was generally
good in the new skyscrapers. Engineering designs had also

conformed to accepted standards. However, Steinbrugge and Lloyd Cluff said, in discussing the role of the reinforced concrete in the destruction brought on by the tremor, "damage to re-inforced concrete frames at their joints showed an absence of confining steel. While this is considered to be poor practice by some authorities, it nevertheless is a commonly followed practice in much of the United States."

Two years after Caracas, the next moderate earthquake struck Santa Rosa, seriously damaging brand-new reinforced-concrete buildings, including one recently completed by Sonoma County to house its social-services departments. The experience of the Santa Rosa Social Services Building, which cost almost half a million dollars to repair, Karl Steinbrugge, William Cloud, and Nina Scott concluded, "is not at all re-assuring when extrapolated to reinforced concrete high rise frame construction." The three investigators concluded that "there is an increasing number of high rise reinforced concrete frame structures being built throughout metropolitan San Francisco, Los Angeles and other western cities. Based on the 1969 Santa Rosa experience and the 1967 Caracas experience and the 1964 Alaskan experience, collapse of one or more of these modern high rise reinforced concrete frame structures in a great earthquake would not be a surprise."

A number of structural-engineering firms try to steer their customers away from concrete frames in any building more than seven or eight stories high, especially if the building is to be placed on ground of dubious quality. Many structural engineers place a twelve- or thirteen-story limit on buildings they design with reinforced-concrete frames, no matter how solid the ground or how hard the concrete industry still tries to convince them that they are being too conservative. The tests that have been conducted on reinforced concrete, the holdouts say, have simulated earthquakes of only a few sec-

onds' duration. And while an earthquake lasting only five or
ten seconds would leave a reinforced-concrete structure intact, prolonged shaking in a moderate earthquake or long
shaking—forty to fifty seconds, a likely possibility—in an intense and severe earthquake might have devastating effects
on the reinforced concrete. In some cases, they say, the
shaking could crack the frame. Then, as the earthquake vibrations continue, the cracked concrete could grind away at
the reinforcing steel until the steel collapsed under the assault. "Both strength and ductility are required," Henry Degenkolb summarizes. "Present specifications for concrete
buildings in particular permit details of steel re-inforcing
that are not appropriate in seismic areas although they are
accepted in the present codes."

Although Degenkolb has doubts about the use of reinforced-concrete frames in high-rise buildings, he likes, however, to use reinforced-concrete shear walls—in effect, huge
slabs of concrete, often as tall as the building itself, that absorb and dispel earthquake energies—in combination with
steel frames. In a moderate earthquake, the reinforced-concrete shear wall alone can absorb and neutralize the earthquake vibrations. During a highly intense earthquake, the
shear wall would bear some of the burden before possibly
cracking under the tremor's forces. In such a case, the
highly ductile steel frame would come into play, resisting
the continued vibrations or swaying and preventing a collapse.

Reinforced-concrete frames, of course, have their defenders. Some engineers argue that the material has been pillo-
ried unfairly and that many of the unfavorable reports on
reinforced concrete have been issued under the aegis of the
steel and iron industry, which obviously stands to benefit
from any shadows cast upon reinforced concrete. As far as
the Portland Cement Association is concerned, if rein-

forced-concrete buildings failed in Caracas, they failed because engineers had not planned for the material properly.
"The quality of construction in Caracas is comparable to
that in the United States," a report by the cement association on the 1967 Caracas earthquake said. "High quality
materials and workmanship were evident in many of the observed structures. . . . It appears that most of the distress
caused by this earthquake would not have occurred if present engineering knowledge of structural behavior in earthquakes had been utilized in the planning and designing of
buildings in Caracas."

A number of engineering experts argue that it is possible
to construct a building badly using a steel frame just as easily as it is to construct it badly by using a reinforced-concrete frame. Olive View Hospital (sometimes cited as San
Fernando's contribution to the damnation of concrete), Dr.
George Housner told a state legislative subcommittee, did
not collapse just because it was a reinforced-concrete structure. The hospital, he said, "had been designed to the minimum requirements of the code, whereas the [smaller] building next to it that survived was actually stronger than the
code required. The difference in strength, [I] attribute
mainly to architectural considerations. In the big building it
was clear that the architect wanted the columns to be small
and did not want solid concrete walls. There were strong
concrete walls in the upper stories, but in the first story,
there were no walls, no shear walls, and the columns were
much smaller than the engineer would normally like to
make them. . . . I am sure that had the engineer been given
the assignment on that building to make sure it wouldn't be
severely damaged, he would have done it differently and
could have made it survive." The fault, this line of reasoning
holds, lay, not in reinforced concrete, but in the way it had
been used. Olive View was one case where fancy architec-

ture and weak engineering had conspired to bring about tragedy.*

Inadequate codes—with their out-of-date approach to earthquake forces, their superficial approach to the use of new materials, and their near-speculative acceptance of new uses for established materials—would constitute no danger if there were a plethora of good engineering in California.

But it is a simple and generally accepted axiom that good engineering is in exceedingly short supply. Many engineers, for example, do not know (or do not care) that the building code as written is a minimal code, that if they are to design and build truly earthquake-resistant structures, they must design them to resist forces greater than 13 percent of their mass weight. Furthermore, as the demand grows for engineers to handle California's burgeoning construction projects, an increasing portion is being assigned to practitioners who come to California from the forty-four states that have no earthquake history and where the engineers have not had to concern themselves with seismic safety. To be sure, many of these engineers are licensed to practice structural engineering. But they are practitioners who naïvely study the local building codes and who assume that the earthquake provisions they contain will guide them to proper engineering designs. As these out-of-state engineers come and go, they quite naturally fail to pick up those additional bits and pieces of information the more knowledgeable local California engineers, as one native practitioner put it, "keep in their heads or pass on to the apprentices of new generations."

Even if the native engineer knows that he must design

* Foes of concrete would of course point out that the third conspirator *was* concrete, because the material *was* prone to abuse.

San Andreas Lake and Crystal Springs Reservoir, lying in the San Andreas fault-zone valley south of San Francisco, where housing developments have been built over the fault zone. The 1906 earthquake fracture of about five feet displacement followed a line from bottom center of the view for almost eighty miles into the distance. (U.S. Geological Survey)

A stream in the Carrizo Plain that has been offset approximately one-fourth mile by the San Andreas Fault. (U.S. Geological Survey)

View looking north along the Elkhorn Scarp, San Andreas fault zone. The Carrizo Plain is to the left; the Elkhorn Plains are to the right. (U.S. Geological Survey)

A housing development takes form in the San Andreas fault-zone valley west of Palmdale. Photographed in May, 1965. (U.S. Geological Survey)

Lower Van Norman Reservoir after the San Fernando earthquake of February 9, 1971. Seismic shaking caused failure of the dam; the concrete dam facing and service road have slid with a portion of the dam into the reservoir. There is extensive fracturing on the remaining front of the earth-fill dam. The previous water level can be seen on the concrete facing; considerable water had been emptied by the time of the photograph. A second intake tower has toppled and is submerged. Oblique air view looking east. (U.S. Geological Survey)

Oblique air view southeast of collapsed structures at interchange of Highways 5 and 210, San Fernando; after the earthquake of February 9, 1971. The Southern Pacific Railroad was both broken and displaced. The off-ramp at upper left did not collapse until the day after the earthquake. The pier supporting the superstructure over the railroad track was damaged at its base by seismic shaking and failed at its base, at a rate of about two feet per three hours. (U.S. Geological Survey)

Olive View Hospital, San Fernando, after the earthquake of February 9, 1971, showing ambulances crushed by collapsed buildings. (U.S. Geological Survey)

In this picture of the Skinner barn west of Olema after the 1906 California earthquake, the fault passes under the barn to the right of center. The main part of the barn remained on its foundation; the shed at right was dragged fifteen feet. (U.S. Geological Survey)

past the requirements in the code and even if the knowledge sometimes does filter down to the visiting engineer, the information is useful only when the engineer is allowed to act upon it. The supplementary provisions necessary to increase a building's resistance to earthquake forces means greater expenditures—often an additional 2 or 3 percent of the total cost of construction. The added costs are negligible when compared to the potential cost of repairing or replacing an earthquake-damaged building. Yet many engineers, especially those working on small projects or on buildings constructed for real estate speculation, hesitate to include the added costs in their bids for new business. For many a developer, an additional construction cost of 2 percent represents the margin between profit and loss. Rather than hire the engineer who will go beyond the code, the developer will turn to the man who is content to follow only what the code requires and who will present him with the least expensive construction estimate.

In a very few construction projects, the extra expenditure is approved. "A company intending to occupy a building it is constructing will probably insist that very thorough earthquake engineering be done," the magazine *Mosaic* says. Dr. Housner, testifying before a congressional committee investigating the February 9 earthquake, agreed with the contention that some buildings, usually skyscrapers bearing the proprietor's name, are given lavish construction treatment and may therefore be highly earthquake-resistant. "These buildings," Dr. Housner said, "are costly, and since they are monuments to the owner, special, very special engineering precautions are taken in the design of these buildings."

In the field, incompetent engineering is exacerbated by the sloppy workmanship that is the hallmark of American construction.

Experts who studied Alaskan buildings in 1964 were appalled by what they found. "Buildings as erected," Herman Light, an architect who visited Alaska, reported in the *Journal of the American Institute of Architects*, "bore little or no indication of compliance with [the] code." Lack of attention to proper connections, designs, calculations, and detailing was found to be common practice rather than the exception, Light said. In many buildings, no bonds between concrete and reinforcing steel could be seen. One multistory apartment building erected with a steel frame and concrete filler walls, Light wrote, was a shambles. The filler walls were composed of two thicknesses of concrete blocks, separated by rigid insulation board. Light could find no dowels to the beams or to the columns. The walls, Light said, actually peeled off layer by layer, prior to collapsing.

"Designs were being produced everywhere by everyone. Work was being scheduled more on how fast it could be done than how well it could be done. Hurry! Hurry! Poor quality concrete ingredients and the lack of bond to reinforcing steel was readily apparent in most concrete structures; structural steel failures indicated a lack of care in detailing; and the performance of pre-cast concrete and lift-slab structures was completely unsatisfactory," Light wrote.

According to a study of the Alaska damage conducted by the California Department of Water Resources,

a very large percentage of the structural damage were direct results of inadequate quality control of construction and lack of adherence to building codes and specifications. In one case, structural failure was attributed to a revision made after the structure was built by the owner without the advice of the structural engineer. The owner made openings in the shear walls for doors and as a result weakened the later resistance of the structure.

California is no less susceptible to construction-site deficiencies. Many small and medium-size buildings, for example, are built of unit masonry—materials ranging from rocks to red brick to hollow concrete blocks. When these hollow concrete blocks are used in the construction of walls, they should be used in combination with steel reinforcing rods and poured concrete. That is, once the blocks are placed, the steel rods should be run through the hollows of the blocks, linking them together. Concrete should then be poured into the spaces to keep the rods in place. The combination of steel and concrete theoretically adds strength to such unit-masonry walls. Yet often the hollows are not filled adequately (or not filled at all), and reinforcing steel rods are left out or badly placed.

At other times, workmen on the site improvise techniques they feel will make for better construction, without consulting the engineer in charge of the building. "Sometimes somebody on the construction decides that the reinforcing steel in concrete needs rustproofing," David Leeds says. "So they spray the steel with an antirust solution that effectively prevents proper bonding between the steel and the concrete." The result of the well-intentioned but misguided move is a weak and earthquake-hazardous slab or pillar of concrete. "It's a problem," says Ed O'Connor, director of the Long Beach Department of Building and Safety, "to get the information detailed in the plans incorporated in the construction."

Construction abuses are minimal in areas where there are strong inspection departments. However, good inspection in California, especially northern California, is often the exception and not the rule. In some cases, no inspections of new construction are made, especially when buildings constructed with public funds are raised. Until late 1971, for example, when the Sonoma County Board of Supervisors finally passed the necessary legislation, no county department had the power to inspect the construction of public buildings. Many building departments are so strapped for funds and properly trained personnel,° says Henry Degenkolb, that the average building department is lucky if it can keep up with construction of new residences or if it can, on occasion, catch a major error in a large structure. "An engineer might spend six months designing a big project," Degenkolb says, "and the city building department has to check it out in a matter of days."

The inspection problem is especially acute in the case of high-rise construction. Because detailed inspection of the thirty- to forty-story buildings is so essential, some major cities are careful to give them the attention they need, even running designs and specifications through computer analysis. And in the case of prestige buildings, the owner will sometimes pay for a structural engineer who will do nothing but carry on constant surveillance. Detailed investigations revealed in time the development of tiny cracks in the steel framework of the $175 million, fifty-two-story twin towers being constructed in downtown Los Angeles for the Atlantic Richfield Corporation. The cracks, which occur when unusually heavy metal is welded under strain for a prolonged amount of time, could have affected the towers' performance during a strong earthquake.

But while these cracks were discovered and repaired, the uneasy suspicion lingers that similar defects in large buildings built for speculation go undetected or, if they are detected, are routinely covered up. The inspection of high-rise construction projects, says Henry Degenkolb, may be especially troublesome in smaller towns and suburban areas. "In the outlying districts when you get high rises," he says, "they will be inspected by a well-educated carpenter or

° Almost no building departments require structural- or civil-engineering backgrounds or degrees for inspection personnel. In the early sixties, the building inspector in Anchorage was a retired mining engineer, David Leeds says.

plumber. For an average building he would be fine, but for a high rise, he is not even in the ball park."

Because inspections are costly, the engineering profession has tried to find other ways to guarantee that the products they use in building meet the standards and specifications they set. For example, engineers and contractors using structural steel for building frames decided to accept certificates from steel mills stating that the supplied steel meets the strength and composition requirements set for them by the structural engineer. Engineers always felt at ease with the system because they received their steel directly from the nation's major steel producers. However, there are signs here and there that the system might be fraught with problems. In recent years, contractors have begun to buy steel from wholesalers and dealers, some of whom may not be scrupulous in supplying the steel the engineer wants.

According to one engineer, John Brown of Santa Rosa, one such wholesaler supplied him with $75,000 worth of faulty steel. When the steel arrived, there was nothing to arouse his suspicion. But because it had been slated for use in a vital facility, Brown says, he decided to run independent tests on randomly picked samples. Even as the testing began, Brown was in for a surprise. The steel had come to Santa Rosa with the traditional markings of U.S. Steel, Bethlehem, and Inland steel. Under preliminary preparations for tests, however, the assorted markings rubbed off, revealing beneath them the trademarks of Nippon steel. Tests carried out by a laboratory hired by Brown determined that the beams that the dealer claimed were made of solid steel were in truth composed of laminated sheets of steel. The sheets were interlaced by an ample supply of air bubbles. The tests also revealed the steel to be a full 25 percent below the strength indicated on the certificates sent by the dealer.

Nippon, Brown thinks, probably sold factory seconds to the dealer at a substantial discount. But the dealer, an eye on an easy profit, tried to sell the steel as full-strength, quality steel by using forged American mill certificates. The wholesaler, Brown said, first insisted that the whole matter had been a mix-up and then maintained that the tests run by Brown's laboratory and corroborated by a second laboratory were wrong. In any case, Brown says, when the dealer found that the steel was being tested, he refused to ship him any more supplies.

Brown says that he has warned other structural engineers to test steel obtained from wholesalers, a step some have begun to take. While the independent testing would add to the cost of construction, Brown says, the more immediate worry is the potential effect substandard steel, used in buildings erected before the fraudulent dealings were discovered, would have. "A little while after my experience I ran into a San Francisco engineer who told me that, in putting up a high rise, he found that he had gotten some laminated steel from a wholesaler though he had ordered solid beams," Brown says. "He didn't think anything of it and said that he just used the steel in parts of the building where he thought it would not play a crucial part. He thought it would be all right since the certificates said it was up to strength. But I asked him if he had had the steel tested for strength and he said, 'No, why?' When I told him of my experience, I could see the blood drain from his face."

PART III

The People Who Live in Earthquake-Riddled Land

Chapter Eight

It is nearly six o'clock in the morning and, while most of the San Fernando Valley is still asleep, here and there families are beginning to stir. On this February 9, 1971, Cindy (not her real name) is just taking her first sip from a steaming cup of coffee. Her four children are sound asleep and her husband is finishing his shower. Suddenly, the house begins to shudder, and before Cindy can grasp its meaning, the shudder escalates into a formidable, drawn-out convulsion, throwing her to the floor. As she cowers helplessly, dishes fly out of their cupboards. The refrigerator, trapped between sink and counter, violently throws open its door and fires bottles, vegetables, meats, and fruits into the room. The television flies off its stand, and glass seems to be exploding everywhere. The children are crying, and, as her stumbling husband tries to make his way toward her, Cindy begins to scream.

Almost as suddenly as it came, the earthquake disappears, and the family, assured all are safe, begins to calm itself down. The day is spent assessing the damage, cleaning the house, straightening its furnishings.

In the days that follow, Cindy, calm and collected, slowly manages to bring the household back to normal. But on the fifth day, the Sunday after the earthquake, the thirty-five-year-old housewife begins to change. Driving to see friends, she freezes at the steering wheel, and when she arrives at her destination, it takes three men to pry her hands off the wheel. In the days that follow, Cindy turns increasingly cool toward her husband, spurning his sexual advances. Nearly two weeks after the earthquake, she spends nearly a full night staring at the ceiling. At dawn, when she feels her husband awakening, she tells him that she wants out of their eighteen-year marriage. She wants a divorce. "My wife told me," Cindy's husband says later, "that the earthquake made her realize her life was not all it should have been. She says when she was lying on the kitchen floor, she realized she 'never really had a chance to live.' "

As the earthquake tore its way across the San Fernando Valley, the scenario played out by Cindy and her husband was only a small part of an invisible devastation, ill-defined and badly understood, that accompanied in various forms and shapes the physical destruction readily apparent to the eye. Adults and children, men and women would come into the grips of emotional upsets—depressions, amnesia, assorted hysterias that ranged from the mild to the severe. "For nights after the earthquake I had trouble sleeping," Victor S., a thirty-one-year-old accountant said. "I found myself going to bed and lying down as lightly as possible so that I could bolt out of the room at the slightest shudder. During the day it felt like I was always sitting on the edge of the chair ready to run. Even vibrations from the refrigerator turning on and off were enough to make me jump."

Victor regained his composure after a few days, but others were not so lucky. One divorced mother of two, a woman named Lee, found herself huddled in her children's bedroom during the severe shaking. For almost a month after the earthquake she could not sleep, allowing herself only catnaps on the living-room couch, and then only if she was fully clothed and had left all the lights on. Another psychological victim of the quake, a forty-year-old man, also slept with his clothes on—and for weeks piled warm clothing near the front door to grab in case he had to hurtle out into the cold during another earthquake.

One young woman in her early twenties froze with fear in her bed while the earthquake throttled her home. "After that I couldn't get myself to go back into that room," Peggy says. "Not for sleeping, not for anything. In fact, I had all my clothes moved to another room. I finally decided that it was absurd and went to a doctor for help." It took a therapist several weeks to help Peggy through her newly acquired phobia. "First, he had me think pleasant thoughts about the room. Then, after a while, he got me to go into the room for a few minutes to do things in there I enjoyed doing. I like eating, so I began to have some meals in there. Then finally, he had me stay up one night all night and then go into the room for a catnap at dawn. After that it got easier."

A number of marriages like Cindy's collapsed after the earthquake, especially where the couple had been having problems before the disaster. One young couple, David and Mary M., had been quarreling and drifting apart even before February 9. Hoping to save their marriage, they had been seeing a marriage counselor, trying to sort out their problems. When the earthquake struck, David was on his way to work and Mary was caught alone at home. Later, when the cleanup period was under way, David spent more time helping his parents repair their damaged home than he spent helping Mary put their own damaged house back in order. The resentments Mary had felt surfaced again, and soon after the tremor, the marriage was near dissolution.

Why did the earthquake—like other disasters, including tornadoes, hurricanes, and explosions—engender psychological reactions that were to last beyond a few seconds of frantic heartbeats? What happens in an individual's mind when he sees his community and his immediate environment devastated by cataclysm?

Some anthropologists define man as an animal who had differentiated himself from his fellow creatures by learning to build an intricate and complicated culture. As he conceives and changes his culture and as he adds new rules and regulations, the culture comes to resemble a complicated maze. As long as the culture-maze functions and as long as man is able to live in it in peace with himself and the others who share the maze with him, man is happy. In fact, he can be happy just sitting in one corner of the maze, doing nothing new, adding no new corridors, while he stares out with contentment at the rest of the world. "Man, in other words, falls in love with his maze and his way of running it," one anthropologist says. But if a disaster comes along and destroys his maze, whether in whole or in part, man is distressed. Not only is there physical destruction all around, but all normal, business-as-usual routines are interrupted and severely hampered. He suddenly is convinced that the elaborate cultural superstructure he has constructed is totally inoperative and ineffective. His world has been destroyed and he is left standing in the cold world, naked and unprotected.

Left unprotected to deal with a harsh world, the inhabitant of a maze could be reduced to bizarre behavior. But while the disaster's forces have worked to strip him of his warm and secure outer haven, his safe and nestlike maze, the disaster has also worked to disrupt some vital workings that are part of his inner being.

Man, like other animals, is geared to react automatically to danger. That is, as he grows and develops, he encounters daily threats—some minor, some not so minor—to his health and safety. And as he does, cumulative experience teaches him how to cope with a particular threat, should he meet it again later in life. If and when he does run into familiar trouble, almost as soon as he has perceived the danger, his brain picks out an appropriate set of automatic responses and begins to mobilize the body for action—be it fight or flight. In other words, if he sees a child careening carelessly toward him on a bicycle, if he sees a fist flying at his nose, if he sees another man bigger than he is leaping at him, he does not have to stop and think "aha, I'd better get out of that kid's, fist's, or man's way." Whatever he does, he does instinctively.

There are times, however, when the danger is so overwhelming, when the source of the danger is so sudden and unfamiliar—as in a severe earthquake—that the threatened individual is unable to respond. The brain has assessed the presence of danger and has even begun to mobilize some nervous- and muscular-system reactions. But at the same time, the individual's conscious mind reels in confusion over the strange and unprecedented threat. As he tries to make some sense out of the situation, indecisiveness begins to set in. Suddenly, fear, which has been only one component of the automatic reflexes that would have enabled the individual to stand and fight (or to flee) known and familiar dangers, becomes an overwhelming and paralyzing emotion. His understanding of the threatening danger lessens rapidly, and he is soon reduced to virtual helplessness, incapable of making even the slightest decision. The body, which in semiautomatic drive has been primed for action, literally gets tired of spinning its defensive wheels and begins to dampen the nervous and muscular energy it has been holding at the ready. Thus, confronted by the danger, incapable of taking action, the individual begins to feel weak and dizzy, struggling to breathe, even finding it difficult to talk.

The disaster's assault on a man or woman, on the individual's surroundings, thus can reduce the person to a childish, helpless being, incapable of responding to questions, sometimes indifferent even to painful wounds. A withdrawal from the real world and an unwillingness to deal with its new everyday challenges for a time after the disaster are the only sure method the stricken individual has of coping with a situation exceeding comprehension.

The individual's entanglement with the disaster does not begin and end with a simple emotional withdrawal from its threat or from its results. In many instances, a person touched by a widespread disaster personalizes it. That is, the individual makes the catastrophe his very own private possession, an occurrence inextricably linked to him and him alone. Perhaps one of the most objective and striking examples of this phenomenon came from William James, the famous psychologist. James, who at the turn of the century had been teaching at Harvard, was in California in 1906, having committed himself to lecture at Stanford. When a colleague at Harvard heard that James was leaving for California, he jokingly told the psychologist that perhaps "they'll give you a touch of earthquake while you are there." James wrote later:

> When lying awake at about half past five on the morning of April 18 in my little "flat" on the campus of Stanford, I felt the bed begin to waggle, my first consciousness was one of gleeful recognition of the nature of the movement. "By Jove," I said to myself, "here's

B'ssold earthquake after all!" And then, as it went *crescendo*, "And a jolly good one it is too," I said.

Sitting up involuntarily, and taking a kneeling position, I was thrown down on my face as it went *fortior*, shaking the room exactly as a terrier shakes a rat. Then everything that was on anything else slid off to the floor, over went bureau and chiffonier with a crash, and the fortissimo was reached.

I discerned retrospectively certain peculiar ways in which my consciousness had taken in the phenomenon. First, I personified the earthquake as a permanent individual entity. It was <u>the</u> earthquake of my friend B's augury, which had been lying low and holding itself back during all the intervening months, in order, on that lustrous April morning, to invade my room. . . . It came, moreover, directly to *me*. It stole in behind my back, and once inside the room, had me all to itself, and could manifest itself convincingly. . . . All whom I consulted on the point agreed as to this feature in their experience. "It expressed intention." "It was vicious." "It was bent on destruction." "It wanted to show its power."

When the witness to a disaster ascribes a personality to the catastrophe and links the catastrophe to himself, a mental labyrinth is entered in which a host of guilts and angers intertwine to haunt the disaster victim, whether or not he is personally injured or affected financially. "Where there is a chronic threat," one anthropologist has written, "that threat will take on meaning far above and beyond its real and inherent nature. The event which is threatened will have causes, and all human beings are vain enough to see causes in themselves. The chronic threat, the catastrophe that is long awaited, takes on distinct meanings and provides a

focus for long standing anxieties, guilts, fears and hostili-
ties."

On one level, the disaster survivor may imagine that the
disaster was sent to be his own special punishment for some
real or fancied religious or social transgression. On still another level, the disaster victim tries to spare himself the
wrath of the disaster by making himself a part of it. That is,
he fancies himself part of the power that brought on the disaster. In this process, he also develops pangs of guilt, because now he is actively responsible for the destruction and
havoc wrought by the disaster. On yet a third level, the disaster victim may feel anger toward the disaster itself and,
knowing that this is irrational, directs his anger at husband
or wife, God, the police, or any other close governmental
authority. And since anger, felt and expressed against others, is frowned upon in our society, the disaster victim again
begins to feel pangs of irrational and self-destructive guilt,
this time over the anger he senses welling up in him.

The feeling among disaster victims that they or their community have been designated specifically for punishment is
a universal phenomenon. After the July, 1963, earthquake in
Skopje, Yugoslavia, researchers interviewing townspeople
found a significant number of men and women telling them
that the tremors had struck Skopje because "people in
Skopje lived too well," "they had grown much too con-
ceited," "there was too much building going on," and that
people had been prone to forget "how small and insignificant they were." In the San Fernando Valley earthquake,
guilt anxieties were most vividly seen in children. "Children
think in magical ways," Dr. Stephen J. Howard of the San
Fernando Valley Child Guidance Clinic said. "When something like this happens, they sometimes feel responsible.
They have thoughts about things like sex and anger and they
feel guilty about such thoughts. When something bad happens, they sometimes feel responsible. Suddenly they are

awakened and the earth is shaking and they have fantasies that someone is screaming and that they are being punished. For what? For their own bad thoughts."

Dr. Howard cites the case of one thirteen-year-old girl named Janice, who had been a model daughter and student. Yet after the San Fernando earthquake, she fell into a deep desperession, losing her self-confidence and poise, finding herself obsessed with thoughts of suicide. A counselor at the Child Guidance Clinic found that the thirteen-year-old girl had harbored deeply buried fears that she might be able to hurt people if she got angry with them. "The quake," Dr. Howard said, "produced terrific anxiety about what her anger could do, how destructive it could be."

Like ancient tribes, modern-day disaster victims who perceive catastrophe as punishment often see God's hand in the event. In the year after a tornado swept through San Angelo, a small town in western Texas, killing 11 and injuring 150, more than 200 of the town's 1700 pupils suddenly joined the "Youth for Christ" movement. Members of the local high school football team began to attend church regularly, moving en masse from one service to another. Psychologists who interviewed the town residents found that almost 30 percent thought that the storm (and severe weather that came one year after the 1953 tornado) had come as God's punishment. When the researchers asked the town's inhabitants if they felt it would be possible to escape the damage and danger of future storms, almost 27 percent replied affirmatively—and two-thirds of those 27 percent said that prayer and clean living, not man-made precautions, would be the key to safety. "We're lucky that God, the Good Lord, was with us," one woman told researchers after an Arkansas tornado. "We've been good to the church and I believe that goes a long way in the Lord taking care of you. . . . My son in Judsonia and his family was saved, and I believe it's because he went to church and tried to live right."

The belief that God metes out disasters is not limited to any part of the country, or any particular religious group or sect. When a volcanic eruption in early January, 1960, terrorized Kapoho, Hawaii, with spewing lava, fire, and earthquakes, all of which seemed to grow more intense every day, the island's inhabitants, many of Chinese descent, came to the site of the eruptions bringing traditional Hawaiian offerings of breadfruit, bananas, pork, and tobacco to mollify Pele, the goddess thought responsible for the eruptions. The supplicants brought their offerings in boxes still adorned with Christmas wrapping paper and ribbons. Thus, the Reverend Billy Graham was able to tell an Oakland, California, audience recently that "God uses earthquakes to shake people up, out of their complacency and overconfidence. Some earthquakes are natural, but sometimes when God wants to get a point across, He speaks through earthquakes."

If the individual tries to equate a natural disaster with punishment for moral transgressions—his or the community's—he begins on a path that leads into dangerous blind alleys. If the survivor has escaped, his body and personal belongings unscathed, he must assume that he was among the righteous of the community. In fact, psychologists say, the compelling desire to show that the righteous were spared leads to the awed recital and accounts of the inspiring way in which churches, altars, crucifixes, and religious personnel were also spared by the disaster.

After the February 9 earthquake, a *Los Angeles Times* story exalted the survival of a small interdenominational chapel on the grounds of the San Fernando Veterans Administration Hospital. Amid the ruins of the hospital, the story said, the chapel stood unchallenged. "There is an eerie sense of peace and quiet inside the small stucco building, which stands out amid the rubble," the story almost whispered. "A small sign outside the door reads 'Enter, rest and pray.' Eight beautiful stained glass windows, which line the sides of the chapel, were not even cracked when the earth beneath the hospital began to shake, collapsing two buildings and claiming the lives of at least 39 patients and employes.

"The windows tell the story of Christ."

On the other hand, the disaster survivor, confronted by incontestable evidence that sinners were not the only ones to die or suffer injury or that confirmed sinners escaped the disaster's wrath, is left with the unenviable task of working out a rationale for the pattern of punishment. "I just believe, I guess, there is some good people blowed away but there is some that wasn't all right," an Arkansas woman told visiting psychologists after a tornado. "Still if they was going to take the people that wasn't living right, looks it'd took this depot outfit down here. That's always lived down there. I've said several times I jut look for a bad storm to strike this town and blow that thing away. But it never touched it. But was so near—funniest thing in the world."

If the evil were spared but not the righteous, then God was either capricious or cruel in his dispensation of punishment. This reasoning leads the survivor to be angry with God—obviously an unacceptable, uncomfortable, and guilt-inducing thought. On the other hand, if God was free from blame, then the righteous dead suddenly assume a holier-than-thou attitude over the survivor: they, in one last act of goodness, have chosen to sacrifice themselves to spare others from death. The realization that some good people have chosen to sacrifice themselves, and in the process have become even *more* righteous, also makes the survivor angry. But just as quickly, he begins to feel great pangs of guilt over the anger directed at someone who has died. This suffusion of anger-guilt engendered by the dead, however, is not the last stop in the confusion of emotions. The disaster over, the survivor realizes that during the catastrophe he ardently wished that he be spared. The wish, he thinks later, could only have meant that someone else then had to die, that someone else had been killed to be his substitute on the mysteriously assigned quota of deaths in a disaster. Once again, he begins to feel pangs of irrational guilt.

If the disaster has brought a heavy death toll, the survivor's anger at the victims—and his guilty feelings about that anger—is again multiplied by contradictory attitudes he holds toward death. On the one hand, the dead, having left life to enter a highly mysterious state, assume a supernatural power and sheen. But at the same time, having succumbed to a disaster others were able to survive, the dead become pitiful creatures, pathetic and below contempt. However, looking at the dead, the survivor suddenly realizes that he too is mortal, that he will also die some day. Anger once again wells up in the survivor. Why should the dead take it upon themselves to remind him of a mortality he would just as soon ignore? Furthermore, not only have these dead abandoned him, not only are they reminding him of his frailty, but now they also have the nerve to lie around and demand special care and burial—at the very time the survivor would rather be going about the business of rebuilding his own life.

One anger cascades over the other, each bringing with it a mortifying guilt. In effect, says Dr. Stanley Rosenman, a psychologist, disaster survivors pay a double toll to calamity. First, they are roundly shaken by the disaster itself, and the terrors that accompany it, for a few brief seconds or minutes. Then, once the initial moments of terror pass, the disaster survivors fall into a state of self-harassment as they move through the cycles of anger and guilt induced by their irrational perception of the events that have shaken their lives. "All too often," says Dr. Rosenman, "a dejected apathy—defense against, an expression of, and atonement for the guilt—debilitates the individual long after disaster has passed, lacerating anew his unhealed wounds and unnerving him for any effort at improvement of his situation."

Not everyone suffers from the guilt and anger syndrome, and, if they do, they do not suffer in the same way or to the same extent. Nor, for that matter, is guilt always irrational or unavoidable.

Psychologists point out that in any disaster situation, there are people in a city or town who, by virtue of their jobs, will be torn between helping their families when disaster strikes or staying at their posts, working to save and help the community. Firemen, policemen, rescue workers, and others invariably have to choose, and the choice they make —invariably tinged with some degree of guilt—will affect the community's ability to get back on its feet. For example, when two freighters blew up in Texas City, Texas, killing 570 people and leveling every building within a half mile of the port, most men were at work in local oil refineries, away from their families. Initially, many of the men, faced by the dilemma of whom to serve, resolved it in favor of their families, leading to some confusion and disorganization in the moments immediately after the thundering explosions. On the other hand, most of the workers at the refineries stayed at their jobs, sensitive to the possibility that further explosions and fires could start if they deserted their posts. Thus, if some of the men felt badly about not rushing home, the guilt was mitigated by the realization that adherence to duty had avoided further catastrophe.

There are times when those trapped in such dilemmas can resolve them in favor of the community and yet suffer little because they did not turn immediately to their families or close friends. Unconsciously, they realize that, in the long run, their decisions will help everybody. "As I drove around town after the tornado had passed," a state patrolman told psychologists investigating a wind storm's effects on a town, "I realized that the best thing I could do was to try to make contact with the outside and get help from there. I started out to drive to the next town and try to call from there. As I drove out of town, people I knew very well would call me by name and ask me to help them find their relatives. Driving by not stopping to help those people who were looking to me as a friend was one of the hardest things I ever had to do."

Public officials or key rescue workers, caught in a community-family dilemma, in fact are too busy for too long to be caught up in moments of full-blown guilt pangs. And by the time they can turn their thoughts to the moment of catastrophe and the choices they made in its wake, the irrational guilt feelings that may accompany the decision of putting strangers above family may no longer be potent or even be stirring. For example, a Los Angeles fireman, who was heavily involved in the disaster-relief work after the February 9 earthquake and who had to leave his family alone, found his reactions to the quake buried until they were shaken loose by an aftershock some time after the original tremor. "We were all sitting around talking about the earthquake, naturally, when the house started to shake and everyone started for the doors. I just sat there in the chair. For some reason, I didn't move. That night I lay awake until five in the morning, trying to sleep. I kept thinking about the original quake. And I could suddenly see everything, hear every noise, see every glass break, reliving again the sound of my wife screaming my name." Having participated in the rescue of survivors from the collapsed San Fernando Hospital, the fireman had been buttressed against any doubts—including guilt feelings—he might have felt about leaving his family behind by the satisfaction of having meaningful work to do in the days after the earthquake.

After many disasters, apathy often strikes many in a community, and some psychiatrists and psychologists feel that it is a natural listlessness accompanying the disaster victims' struggle with their irrational feelings of anger and guilt. Psychiatrists, however, are far from agreement on the subject. Some suggest that the observed passivity is nothing more than a natural reaction, because few members of any community are trained to undertake meaningful activity in a postdisaster period. Instead, they can only sit back and stare.

Nor have psychologists been able to agree on the numbers of people who are usually affected by apathy, whatever its causes. Some investigators have suggested that apathy may affect from 33 to 75 percent of a disaster-struck population. Others have suggested that perhaps no more than 15 or 20 percent of the people touched by a disaster dissolve into apathy and withdrawal. After the Skopje earthquake, Yugoslav psychologists found that only 25 percent of the surviving population could be counted on to help actively in the postdisaster period. For example, of twenty truck drivers hired to take bodies to a cemetery, the psychologists said, only four were still at work a few hours later. "Other people called upon to perform every day routine jobs," they said, "were similarly vulnerable."

The Yugoslavs also suggested that the apathy shown by the Skopje residents might have been contagious. The psychologists noted, for example, that relief teams which came into Skopje as a unit from the outside world were able to function fairly efficiently in the cleanup operations. However, when individual helpers came into Skopje and joined rescue teams formed with local individuals, the outsiders were soon subject to the same apathy that invariably felled the native workers.

The psychologists who argue that people stand around

doing nothing after a disaster precisely because there is nothing for them to do point out that when tornadoes, hurricanes, or earthquakes hit primitive societies, everyone pitches in to help. In tending to the wounded, for example, members of less-specialized societies are not apt to worry about who has and who does not have the proper medical training to help the ailing. "It is a doctor's job to fix broken people," one psychologist has pointed out in talking about observed passivity among more "civilized" disaster victims, "and practicing medicine without a license or good training in first aid is wrong. Hence people stand around and stare not only because they don't know what to do but also because they have been trained not to know and to leave these things to the experts. Perhaps equally important is the impotence that may be felt by the person who sees need for action and is nevertheless trained not to act. He must defend himself against this and he does so by apathy and he looks as if he were in a daze."

"Society tends to delegate roles to a few individuals, and as a result the masses tend to feel helpless," Dr. Edward Stainbrook, chairman of the Department of Human Behavior at the University of Southern California (USC) Medical School, says. "But you have to create meaningful roles for people to play and get them to play those roles even if you have limited resources. One problem of an earthquake in an urban setting is that only a few feel they have the skills necessary to help and the rest are left with a feeling of helplessness." Thus, Dr. Stainbrook suggests, disaster-relief agencies should have people on their staffs charged with finding ways to involve disaster survivors in the postdisaster recovery and reconstruction period.

Some psychologists suggest that the severe emotional reactions to disaster may be avoided by giving vent to one of two natural reactions: the desire to express anger at the disaster itself and the need to talk about the catastrophe after it has struck. One Los Angeles psychologist, Dr. Donald F. Cowan, suggests that when an earthquake strikes, for example, people should begin to shout, curse, clench their jaws, shake their fists, and order the earthquake to stop. The "exercise," which Dr. Cowan says should be done out loud (but is also helpful if carried out only mentally should the individual find himself in a crowd during an earthquake), effectively prevents internal anger from accumulating and growing out of proportion. But talking to the earthquake, ordering it to stop, is also important, Dr. Cowan adds, because in time the earthquake *does* stop. As a result, the frightened individual is given a sense of control over disastrous events, a feeling he does not normally have. Indian rain dances, the baseball hurler's peculiar pitching-mound rites, the gambler's whispered entreaties to his dice, Dr. Cowan says, are everyday examples of individuals attempting to control the more mundane events in their lives by "talking" to them or trying to control the circumstances preceding their occurrence.

Encouraging people to talk about a catastrophe after it has struck would seem to be a gratuitous piece of advice. People, after all, like to talk about new and exciting events even if they are not entirely happy episodes. Yet in a postdisaster situation, many people cannot discuss the catastrophe, especially with children who look to adults for support and understanding of what has just transpired. After the February 9 earthquake, for example, many children found that the adults around them—parents and teachers—acted as if the earthquake had never happened. They did not want to talk about the earthquake, the adults told themselves, because talk would serve only to upset the children further. "Our music teacher pretended the earthquake never happened," one girl complained. "When we wanted to talk about it, she told us to sing. But you can't sing with something like that on your mind."

For children, postdisaster conversations are often important because many may have seen their parents react badly to the catastrophe. When the February 9 earthquake struck, some children awoke, convinced their parents were having a bitter argument. "But children were upset most of all because their parents were frightened," Dr. Stephen Howard says. "In addition this happened in the dark, lights were out, people were stumbling around looking for flashlights, screaming 'stay where you are!' or 'get under a doorway!' And then, most parents made the mistake of running around the house looking for broken things, telling the kids not to move, but leaving them alone." The image that adults are strong pillars of support, in other words, was shattered for many children. Only honest discussion could help the children gain a proper perspective on their parents' behavior and reestablish the normal child-parent relationship.

Psychology's interest in reactions to disasters dates back only to the Second World War, when psychologists began to find some new insights into population behavior that had previously defied explanation, or behavior that had been badly understood. Psychologists, for example, found that the seemingly "ghoulish" flocking of sightseers to a disaster site was more than morbid curiosity. It was, in fact, one way those living in the general area of a catastrophe could come to terms with tragedy. By looking at the damage wrought, psychologists found, the sightseer can work himself up to a slow, careful understanding that he too is mortal. In the process, he steels himself for the possibility of injury or death in a similar, future disaster. But at the same time, viewing the disaster's effects helps the onlooker dispel unreasonable fears about future catastrophes. "Numerous observers mention that there was considerable relief among the British when they discovered what the raids [from German V-2's] were really like," one researcher wrote. "They had expected the attacks to be far more devastating than they actually turned out to be. The satisfaction of curiosity about the destruction produced by an air raid is probably one of the ways in which grossly exaggerated expectations and fantasies were brought into line with reality."

Psychologists were also surprised to find that large-scale bombings of cities during the war did not result in anticipated mass, hysterical flights by city dwellers to the safer countryside. Studying the reactions of Londoners and other city dwellers subjected to constant bombing, psychologists found that far fewer people than they would have thought left the bomb-marked cities, Allied and Nazi alike. Subsequent studies of natural disasters showed that people who do leave a catastrophe-struck area are moved by reasons not connected with fear of the disaster itself.

According to one study, the 1964 Good Friday earthquake in Anchorage, Alaska, was followed by a discernible increase in traffic along the Alaska-Canada Highway. For example, outbound road traffic between Alaska and Canada was almost the same in March, 1963, and March, 1964. In April of 1963, about sixteen hundred persons left Alaska. But in April of 1964, the month of the great earthquake, more than three thousand persons drove out of the state. The peak day of departures was April 18. Even in May of 1964, car traffic out of Alaska was almost 10 percent higher than it had been in May, 1963.

In the two weeks following the earthquake, air travel from Anchorage to Canada and the United States more than doubled. In April, 1964, the state lost about one thousand persons by air, whereas it had gained almost eleven hundred persons in April, 1963. Departures from the day of the earthquake until the end of June, 1964, exceeded departures during the same period in 1963 by almost five thousand persons.

The peak in the air travel came on days when there were especially severe aftershocks in the Anchorage area, seven and eight days after the main earthquake had struck. "We had only thirty reservations on our night flight," the manager of an airline office said, speaking of a day when there had been an especially severe aftershock. "But after the noon shock, the phone nearly rang off the wall for the rest of the afternoon and evening and the entire flight was filled up." A physician, coincidentally traveling that night, said that "the thing that struck me the most, in addition to the confusion and crowding [at the airport] was that a large percentage of the passengers were women and children. The atmosphere was tense and this tension was communicated to the young children who cried continuously during the boarding and the flight."

All in all, the two men who researched the escape patterns after the earthquake found that about 2 percent of the Alaskan population may have left the state because of the earthquake activity. But, researchers pointed out, fear was not the principal motivation driving some to leave the state. "Analysis of responses of many individuals during psychiatric interviews strongly suggests that many saw in the disaster situation an opportunity to solve personal problems in an 'acceptable' way," the researchers said. "It was temporarily approved to verbalize fear. Fear was used as a reason for leaving even though the true and often subconscious reason was not fright at all." Eventually most of those who had left recognized that escape had not solved whatever problems they had, and they eventually returned to Alaska.

Ultimately the question arises—and usually it is brought up at dinner or cocktail parties by a non-Californian who happens to be in attendance—how the state's inhabitants can live, day in and day out, with the horrendous dangers of earthquakes, how they can live with the pressures of knowing that dark and treacherous faults surround them on every side. How, the visitor asks, can any Californian sleep nights knowing the San Andreas Fault is sitting out there in the dark, silently and steadily gathering force to explode?

The answer, pure and simple, is that probably not one Californian in a million gives more than a passing thought to earthquake faults and earthquakes. In New York, muggings are reported in the press every day. Partygoers regale each other constantly with tales of raped and robbed friends. There are daily reminders that life and safety are tenuous commodities. But in California, earthquakes just do not strike every day. When they do, to be sure, the results are devastating and the reminder is immediate. But as the aftershocks fade and weaken, as the mess is cleaned up and pushed out of the way, the reminder of danger goes with them.

Even when a few Californians do remind themselves that the state is riddled with faults and unsafe land, few drive themselves to despair over the matter. For the man in the street, the weather, the ease of life override the issue of earthquake danger. Even the professionals are essentially at ease with the earthquake. Any number of good structural engineers and competent engineering seismologists and engineering geologists work in buildings or live on land they would never recommend to clients. One leading engineering geologist, a dedicated proponent of earthquake safety, lives high in Bel Air in Los Angeles, in a home precariously perched on a steep hillside. From his house he can, at times, actually look *down* on the smog. At night there is nothing but the stars and a pervasive quiet. "In a good strong shake," he says, leaning over to look down at his very own precipice, "I guess this whole lot could wind up in our neighbor's pool down there someplace. We'd never move. We love the house and we love the area."

"I don't know how we live with earthquakes," one native said recently to a visiting New Yorker. "Maybe we are just better adapted than New Yorkers, who don't feel comfortable unless they can walk down the best-lit street and be afraid of something or other." While the attitude seems flippant, it is not too far off the mark. "There is such a thing as healthy denial," Dr. Donald Cowan says. "It's a defense mechanism that allows us to function, and people learn it whenever they are in a dangerous situation. Men, for example, could not go into battle if they constantly thought, 'Well, I'm going to get killed.'

"If it is true that we are going to have a massive earthquake here, then perhaps the healthy denial is necessary. To dwell on it constantly would be counterproductive."

Dr. Cowan does point out that denial is healthy as long as it helps the individual adjust. The mechanism obviously loses its worth when it lessens a man's or woman's chances of surviving an upcoming catastrophe. Thus, the real irrationality in California is not that men, women, and children do not pile into cars and buses and flee the state in horror. The real problem may be that Californians have perfected the proper defense mechanism of denial into a fine art that blinds them to action that would make it possible to coexist to a reasonable degree with earthquakes. In steadfastly denying the existence of earthquakes in order to maintain their sanity, Californians, unfortunately, also go to the extreme of denying the need for safer schools, safer buildings, and safer land use. In fact, the ultimate problem may very well be that Californians *must* deny the necessity of planning to mitigate earthquakes. To acknowledge the need for planning is to acknowledge the potential for disaster.

A number of psychiatrists and psychologists, in fact, worry that some Californians are paying a price for the outwardly good adaptation to earthquake danger. "There might be a higher incidence of psychosomatic tensions among people who live close to faults," Dr. Cowan says. "These people are functioning with a chronic source of tension. Inside they are always marshaling strength to cope with the expected quake. In the process, they may have little energy left to deal with anything else."

Thus, some mental-health experts would like to see more research done on the effect of earthquakes on mental health because, they say, experience from other disasters can be of only limited value in earthquakes. Earthquakes, thinks Dr. Edward Stainbrook, are different because, unlike other disasters, they tend to mobilize very infantile reactions in people when they do strike. "For one thing," Dr. Stainbrook says, "unlike hurricanes and tornadoes, earthquakes strike completely without warning. In addition, earthquakes disturb one of man's most basic fears, the fear of falling. It is one of the few innate fears we are born with. When the ground on which a man lives begins to move, it tends to make children out of us all."

Also open to investigation is the effect of earthquakes on some of the people who are drawn to California. The state, probably more than any other area, lures a disproportionate number of people who are highly mobile, who have no roots, no idea of permanence, people who even in a benign environment are wary and distrustful. They come to California with high hopes for a new start in life and a new meaning to their existence. Yet in the next brief tremor after their arrival, all the fragile expectations may be shattered, leaving the individual with an even weaker psyche than the one brought to California. "A lot of people are here because this is a second- or third-chance society and because they have failed someplace else," Dr. Stainbrook says. "People come here to seek renewal, to find the ideal life. They find good weather and they find jobs, but they find earthquakes too. So once more for them it may be a matter of once more man never is, but is to be, blessed."

Chapter Nine

That it was the scene of a devastating disaster was immediately apparent to the rescue workers scrambling around the corner of the block. The apartment building to their left had been reduced to a shell, part of its roof torn off, its brick facade strewn about the sidewalk and the street. The small industrial plant next door was blackened with smoke, its interior a heap of twisted and shattered metal. A trace of gas hung in the air and a broken pipe trickled a steady stream of water over an open container bearing the legend WARNING! RADIOACTIVE MATERIAL. From their initial vantage point, the rescuers could not quite tell, but the small one-family home farther down the street seemed to be a shambles as well.

Until they became aware of the moans of the dying and the injured, the startled rescuers had almost forgotten that people also may have been involved. As they began to look more carefully at the site, they could see a leg or an arm protruding from the rubble. At first glance, the random limbs were the only clues to a mangled body beneath a heap of bricks or the badly burned or broken person lying behind a jumble of wood. Just as the rescuers were recovering from the momentary surprise and were moving to help those they could, a scream came from the top of the ravaged apartment building. A hysterical young woman, dressed in tight sweater and miniskirt, shouted down at them, begging to be taken off the roof before the building were to suffer another shock that would topple it completely.

To a man, they rushed to her aid, trampling over the dead and injured in their path.

The "scene" of destruction—complete with broken department-store dummies, live men and women sporting mock wounds, and, from time to time, the maiden in distress to drive home a think-before-you-act lesson—is choreographed regularly by the Pasadena Civil Defense Department to train local policemen, firemen, city utility workers, and even park maintenance crews in the art of disaster rescue and relief.

Pasadena's training program is part of a disaster-preparedness program, generally recognized to be one of the best in the state. Yet while officials in other cities and counties admire the program, few have moved to imitate it. And when other jurisdictions have moved to make similar preparations to meet the next catastrophe, they have moved forward only after great hesitation, following the hallowed rule that minimal energy, time, and money be spent on the efforts.

When the Sonoma County emergency-services coordinator left his post in 1967 to assume another job with the county, the Sonoma Board of Supervisors decided that a full-time emergency-relief coordinator was more a luxury than a necessity. Seeking to save the treasury some money, the board turned the job over to a bureaucrat already saddled with other duties. Overburdened, the man found less and less time to devote to emergency preparations, and by the time the 1969 earthquake struck Santa Rosa, Sonoma's disaster-relief program was defunct. In 1970, the board once more found the willpower to hire a full-time emergency-services coordinator.

San Francisco—the one city in California that has suffered a truly catastrophic earthquake—stumbled along with a ten-year-old plan that had never been exercised and a cumbersome and largely ineffective disaster committee until in 1969 it hired Ed Joyce, the state's chief emergency-planning officer to prepare the city for the ever-threatened repeat performance of the 1906 earthquake. Much of Joyce's plan is geared to a maximum response to a maximum earthquake. "In my plans I am assuming that in an 8.3 earthquake," says Joyce, who keeps the February 9, 1971, desk-calendar page, a "REMEMBER LOS ANGELES" scrawled across it, pinned to a wall in his office, "we would have 350,000 casualties, including 3500 deaths." To meet anticipated earthquake disasters, Joyce has revitalized and streamlined the city's emergency council. He has signed contracts with various groups, including the Civil Air Patrol and the Army Corps of Engineers, calling for an automatic rescue and relief response on their part in case of emergency. He has negotiated with private firms to bulldoze rubble and clear streets after an earthquake without waiting for a call from City Hall. Preparations have also been made to draw water from San Francisco Bay and to maintain 150 reinforced water cisterns throughout the city to prevent repetition of the fires that destroyed the city after the 1906 quake. Should the city be cut off by the collapse of some or all of its bridges, intact sections of the freeways will be used as landing strips for small aircraft. And should Joyce's estimates of deaths not be off the mark, the city's morticians are ready to act as emergency coroners.

Many jurisdictions, of course, claim to have plans. There

are city plans and county plans, state plans and federal plans. And officials brandish plans to coordinate the plans, amend the plans, update the plans. Officials often speak in sonorous terms of the need to orchestrate the immediate postdisaster efforts of various levels of government. Hoping to encourage such coordination, for example, the state legislature passed the California Emergency Services Act. Written with an eye to war, the act requires every county to organize itself into a viable disaster-fighting machine whose key function would be to bring the state, the counties, and, within each county, the towns and cities into close and crucial contact. Perhaps anticipating that other man-made or natural disasters would befall the state more often than international war, the legislature also suggested that the resultant county organizational lines be utilized to facilitate relief work in natural disasters.

The state's counties and the political subdivisions within them have reacted less than enthusiastically to the act. Los Angeles County, for example, has organized itself along the war-oriented provisions of the act, and the seventy-seven cities within the county borders have all passed resolutions concurring with the need for action in wartime. But, according to the Los Angeles County Earthquake Commission, "no agreement or understanding exists among the local governments in Los Angeles County to activate the Los Angeles County Operational Area for emergencies other than war or otherwise to provide for coordination among local governments."

Because damage was restricted to a comparatively small area, the San Fernando earthquake involved only three local jurisdictions—the cities of San Fernando and Los Angeles and the County of Los Angeles. However, it provided some startling case studies in uncoordinated relief activity. The earthquake struck at 5:59 A.M. Yet key local (or state and federal) agencies were slow to receive news that an entire wing of the San Fernando Veterans Hospital had collapsed, trapping, injuring, and killing patients and personnel. First word came to the outside world when a Los Angeles City Fire Department helicopter spotted the collapsed wing while on a reconnaissance flight almost an hour and a half after the earthquake. The County Fire Department, which is responsible for fighting fires and carrying out rescue operations in the unincorporated area where the hospital was located, was not told of the disaster at the hospital until nine o'clock in the morning, three hours after the quake. The Los Angeles County Sheriff did not learn about the collapsed facility until 10:30 A.M.

More than seventy persons were trapped in the ruins of the collapsed hospital wing. Some, like Mrs. Helen Schropp and Mrs. Grace Fields were lucky and were pulled—alive and well—from beneath the rubble only hours after the tremor had struck. But many of the other survivors had to wait long into the day and night to be rescued. One man was not brought out from beneath the rubble until almost two and a half days after the earthquake. "I thought I was dead," Frank Carbonara, a sixty-eight-year-old baker, said. Carbonara, who had just reported to work when the quake struck, had dived under a sink to seek protection from the cascading masonry, bricks, and wood. "There was noise and then darkness and silence. I closed my eyes and waited. I prayed God would forgive my sins. But then after a while I noticed I was still breathing."

Carbonara's rescue was a case of extreme good fortune. But rescue officials could only wonder how many of the other forty-nine victims who died they might have been able to save if the authorities had had prompt notice of the collapse. "We might have saved more lives if only we could have gotten to the disaster sooner," Los Angeles Police Lieutenant Al Fried said later. "When the buildings collapsed at 6 A.M. the natural reaction of people in the area when they heard victims screaming was to do something. But the phones were out and nobody thought to notify the police until a good hour later."

The orchestration of a successful disaster-relief program requires two vital ingredients: a viable communications network that will not be affected by failures in conventional power or by the toppling of land lines in an earthquake and a well-constructed, well-supplied emergency-operations center. In such a center, key officials can meet to use emergency-communications equipment to receive reports from their men in the field and to pass information and crucial guidance on to them. The center also allows key officials to stay in across-the-desk touch with each other, enabling them to consult on problems and developments of mutual concern. Both ingredients are in exceedingly small supply around California.

In the aftermath of the February 9 earthquake, one of the few communications networks to function effectively was the Los Angeles area Hospital Emergency Administrative Radio (HEAR), which links 118 hospitals in the metropolitan sprawl. Through the radio network, which is tested continuously by every shift working in every hospital, the damaged hospitals in the San Fernando Valley were able to find beds in unaffected hospitals for the twelve hundred patients they had been treating. Each damaged hospital broadcast the number of patients it had to transfer out. Furthermore, each hospital could also broadcast instructions for special care each patient would require once he or she had been accommodated in another hospital. As the patients were transferred and as the medical needs of hundreds of persons who were injured in the tremor also became clear, the hospitals unaffected by the quake used HEAR to request specialized medication, lung machines, special-diet meals, heaters, and portable lights. Where expectant mothers had been shocked into premature delivery by the earthquake, hospitals using HEAR were able to quickly locate needed incubators.

Despite HEAR's proven success in the San Fernando earthquake, few communities have moved since February 9, 1971, to take the minimal steps necessary to supply their hospitals with an emergency-communications system. Three years after their own earthquake and one year after San Fernando, public-health officials in Sonoma County and in Santa Rosa, supported by the area's medical community, were still lobbying (with little success) for a system that would free medical facilities from the tyranny of the telephone. "The Board of Supervisors is moving," one Sonoma County health official said about efforts to put two-way radios in county-owned hospitals, "but that is not going to help us if we have a 7.5 earthquake tomorrow. If the Dodgers beat the Giants in the World Series the telephone system in this city [Santa Rosa] breaks down." Santa Rosa's private hospitals also have been having a hard time finding the money to install the two-way radio systems they badly want.

Although experts in rescue work agree that a modern emergency-operations center is necessary to link every party vital to a relief effort—hospitals, law-enforcement agencies, fire departments—less than a dozen communities in California have bothered to take advantage of available federal monies (granted under civil defense legislation) to build the necessary facilities. San Francisco, for example, began to move toward building a one-million-dollar-plus emergency-operations center only in 1971. Even with its devastating experience in 1971 as an object lesson, Los Angeles County has yet to make any commitments toward building centralized emergency headquarters that would gather relief and rescue operations for the county under one roof.

One of the few communities to build itself an emergency-operations center and to put it to good use has been Pasadena. Built beneath one of the city's fire stations, the emergency-operations center—built solidly enough to withstand powerful blows—tectonic or nuclear—is a part of the city's daily operations. The center's giant communications room houses the city's fire and police radio networks, both of which are manned twenty-four hours a day for routine work. In nondisaster times, a second hall nearby serves as a seminar room where various city agencies hold meetings, train new employees, or sponsor conferences.

Were an emergency to strike Pasadena—an earthquake on the nearby San Andreas, for example—the heads of various city agencies and departments and key officials (accompanied by representatives of the press) would converge on the center to assume command of relief operations.

In the room given over to seminars in calmer times, city officials are assigned cubicles where they can work and where they can listen in on their men working in the field. "Through the squawk boxes they can hear what is going on," Ted R. Smith, director of the Civil Defense Department, says. "Through the communications center in the other room they can correct mistakes or make suggestions. In fact we can do a great deal in here. We have maps and diagrams that we can project on a screen to keep everyone informed of developments. We even have the capability to shut off water and gas lines on two sides of a street. If you picture a screen like the one that goes on a window, you can imagine how water and gas lines cross a city. Now, if you throw a rock through the screen, you would have an area with a lot of ruptures. Before, if an earthquake had ruptured one part of our 'screen,' we would have had to shut off the gas and water over a large area to prevent escape at the point of the break. Here we can get reports of where the breaks are, look at a diagram and shut off individual lines, at no point farther than a block from the break."

Because the center is used constantly for routine police

and fire department communications, the center's full-time staff is continuously prepared for an emergency. And unlike other cities that have plans and do not rehearse them, Pasadena holds at least one complete disaster exercise every year. "Actually we hold two," says an official at the center only half-jokingly. "The real exercise is provided by a professor at USC. But the Rose Bowl every year gives us a great opportunity to test our disaster work. The city is effectively cut in half by the parade, making it a challenge to get ambulances and fire equipment across it in case it is necessary. A million people come to the parade and more than a hundred thousand to the game, so we have to plan on emergency medical and rest facilities. January 1 is almost enough to keep us in shape."

The lethargic and unorganized responses to earthquake disaster that characterize local relief efforts are matched by a similarly uneven response on the part of various federal and state agencies.

"If you were here on the ninth of February," Father Luis Valbuena, pastor of the Santa Rosa Catholic Church in San Fernando, says in talking about the 1971 earthquake, "you would ask yourself, Is this the first time we have an earthquake in the United States? In a state like this, which has millions and millions, and where we had in 1906 the San Francisco earthquake and the Bakersfield and the Long Beach earthquakes, I was asking myself, who has to be here and is not and why are we not really supported and helped by government agencies?"

The less than adequate response by the various levels of government embittered valley residents. For longer than they felt necessary, they were left to fend for themselves, deprived of even the most essential services. "For days my husband carted water from a neighbor's pool to flush our toilet," Mrs. LaVerne Snell of Sylmar, said. "We had no water for two weeks, for almost a week following the disaster we had no electricity and it was three months before our phone was operative. Where was the Office of Emergency Preparedness available to us? It was available only if we had been able to drive five or six miles down three major streets, over a freeway that was destroyed, and to further complicate our plight, these streets were clogged with emergency equipment, sight-seers and Army of Engineers [*sic*]. Not for days but for weeks."

Various federal agencies bungled their relief work because they were not prepared to communicate in Spanish with San Fernando Valley's large Spanish-speaking community—a curious matter to neglect in a state that is approximately 15 percent Mexican-American. Although several agencies say they had large bilingual staffs ready to help Spanish-speaking disaster victims, Mexican-American community leaders dispute the claim. In the days immediately following the earthquake, community leaders said they had to provide translators to help various government officials cope with the streams of Mexican-Americans (the area hardest hit has a 40 percent Spanish-surname population) who came to the various agencies for help. And while some official literature explaining disaster-aid benefits was available in Spanish, at least one pamphlet read as if it had been prepared by a writer whose knowledge of Spanish dated back to his high school days and extended no further than the nearest English-Spanish dictionary.

The official insensitivity to the immediate postearthquake-disaster needs of the people in the San Fernando area manifested itself in other ways as well. The area had already been affected by the aerospace industry's sliding fortunes and unemployment had been running high. And when the earthquake destroyed scores of businesses, many more people were thrown out of work. Yet unemployment-benefits officials—knowing full well that many persons had no cars and that public transportation was disrupted—refused to open offices at various disaster centers established in San Fernando, Sylmar, and the Santa Rosa Church. "Local officials demanded that . . . disaster programs be administered through their regular offices," a report for the Office of Emergency Preparedness said. "The Unemployment benefits office was already taxed far beyond its work load and physical ability, due to heavy pre-disaster unemployment. Adding the disaster-related unemployment to this office was simply making things worse. We repeatedly asked that four to six U. B. personnel from outside the disaster area be temporarily assigned to the centers but this was never done."

While unemployment officials were fighting suggestions that they set up temporary relief offices in the afflicted area, the Department of Agriculture was dragging its feet on establishing a viable emergency food-stamp program in the Valley. It did not manage to put a food-supply program into operation until February 22, almost two weeks after the earthquake. "By the time plans were completed for such distribution," Robert F. Shea, vice-president of the American National Red Cross, said, "the Red Cross had already met most of the food needs of the disaster victims. Only about forty applications for food stamps were distributed on or after February 22, and of those forty, only seventeen were approved. Yet, during the same thirteen days it took the agencies concerned to determine the need existed, the Red Cross spent hundreds of thousands of dollars to provide individual food orders."

The Agriculture Department's failure to set in motion and maintain a well-prepared machine to tide earthquake victims over their immediate postearthquake food requirements represents but a secondary achievement in federal failure to prepare for the postdisaster needs of its most populous state. The top honors, for ineptitude, however, are reserved for the performance of the Small Business Administration (SBA), an agency that in other, smaller disasters had managed to perform with some credit.

Unfortunately, the SBA (and by extension, the entire federal disaster-relief mechanism) came to the San Fernando Valley assuming that the devastation of an earthquake could be met with the same ease as the damage brought on by a low-grade flood or minor hurricane. As a result, in the early days of the quake the SBA reacted too slowly and too cautiously in helping people with damaged homes. Later, when its turtlelike reaction exposed the SBA to the full fury of an investigating Senate Committee, the SBA tried to make up for lost time. Red tape was cut; the process for dispensing funds was speeded up. At the end of the catch-up period, however, the agency realized that it had wasted millions of dollars. The dissipation was not unnoticed by the press, and, once more, the SBA found itself under attack.

Much of the SBA's immediate postearthquake troubles started because nothing in the enabling legislature that had created the agency and nothing in its own bureaucratic makeup geared it to move quickly in a disaster. And nothing enabled it to distinguish between the needs of an earthquake region and the needs of a hurricane region. Some of the provisions Congress wrote into the SBA act also paved the ground for slow reaction times to disaster. To prevent the SBA finance plans from turning into a give-away bonanza, Congress established the agency as a lending institution. But wanting the SBA to be as helpful as possible, Congress also gave the agency power to forgive up to the first twenty-five hundred of the amount loaned. Nevertheless, SBA officials insisted that the agency's ability to forgive substantial portions of a loan did not change SBA's status as a lending institution. All applications were met with an extensive credit check, even though many people borrowed three thousand dollars or less and had to pay back only five hundred dollars.

The results of the congressional mandates and the SBA interpretation of those mandates resulted in the excruciatingly slow and often inhumane and rude responses. Some SBA officials visited the site of the San Fernando earthquake immediately after the tremor, but a full-scale SBA operation in the valley took almost two weeks to organize. On February 10, thousands of homes were badly in need of immediate repair. But by March 15, 1971, nearly five weeks after the earthquake, the SBA had approved only 118 of almost 2400 applications it had received for loans. By April 16, more than two months after the earthquake, the agency had accepted almost 7000 applications but had approved only slightly more than 1600.

Often, those who needed the money the worst—those who had lost everything—were unable to find help at SBA's doors. Many homeowners who had built or bought houses where the earthquake's fury had been the worst were left with little more than heaps of wood and brick. Despite their best efforts to rebuild their shattered houses, many simply had to walk away from their property. "We purchased a home in 1959," Edward E. Morris of San Fernando said, "and we had built up an equity of $21,000. In a few seconds we lost everything we had worked for all our lives. The house was so cracked, twisted and pulled apart, we could only stare in disbelief. We were finally able to pry the door open and get out. Everywhere we looked there was complete devastation. Every brick wall was down, the driveways had gone clear out into the street. Our cars were dented and banged up though they were garaged."

The Morrises called their insurance man, and like many others found they had no coverage for damage caused by earthquakes. Insurance companies, frightened that they would be wiped out by claims after a severe earthquake, have managed to keep an exceedingly low profile on earthquake-insurance policies. Of the 500 insurance companies that are all too happy to sell other homeowner policies—fire, theft, personal liability—in California, only 187 have earthquake-insurance policies available. But the insurance salesman who will volunteer that his company will write earthquake policies is virtually nonexistent. When they do mention it, many companies will place other obstacles in the homeowner's way. Some firms, for example, will sell earthquake-insurance policies only as riders to their own homeowner packages. Thus, if homeowner Smith has fire and theft insurance with Company A, which will not sell earthquake protection, Company B, which does, will not offer Smith their earthquake protection unless Smith switches his entire account. The penalties involved in canceling and switching policies dissuade many homeowners from exploring the subject further. "We were told the damage to cars was covered," Morris said. "But that is small consolation when you feel you have insurance to protect you against everything."

The Morrises found their way to the SBA office, filled out the application, and attached a contractor's estimate of what it would cost to rebuild the house on the same spot—$19,373. But because geologists had advised the SBA that the area in which the Morris home had stood would still be prone to severe earth movements in future tremors, the Morrises' application to rebuild was turned down. The only alternative was to relocate. But again, the Morrises were trapped. To relocate, SBA would loan them only the amount of their equity in the ravaged home—$21,000—or the builder's estimate for fixing the destroyed house. "What can you buy for $20,000?" Morris asked. "There would have had to be more than one loan, which we cannot afford." Four months after the earthquake, the Morrises were still without a home of their own. "Nothing had been solved, no assurances of any help from anyone. After filling out stacks of paper we had gotten nowhere."

The unemployed, the elderly, and the poor were also cut off completely from the SBA program. "Disaster victims who were unemployed or on public welfare were not issued applications for loans," Robert Shea said. "In an area affected by unemployment in the aerospace industries, this was quite a blow." According to John Steel, president of the Sylmar Civic Association, "an eighty-year-old lady was declined because she could not pay back the loan. They told her she would not live long enough to cut it down to the size she could accommodate."

In mid-1971, SBA officials reviewed their rigid approach to loan applications and tried to cut through some of their own red tape. One early SBA rule had required homeowners applying for loans to present three independent cost estimates of the damages to their homes. By summer, officials were asking for only one estimate. Deluged by a backlog of more than fifty thousand applications, SBA officials supplemented the appraising staff they used to verify homeowner claims by hiring out-of-work aerospace engineers.

Unfortunately, the makeshift operation, refashioned to deal with the crush of business, was no more successful. The first inkling of new trouble came in the fall of 1971. While applications to the Los Angeles office had been averaging about one hundred a week until late summer, the office suddenly found itself swamped under a tide of applications that brought in almost three thousand applications for loans every week. Since many of those applications were for exactly three thousand dollars, the suspicion arose that many Los Angeles homeowners had suddenly come to understand the full import of the widely advertised twenty-five-hundred-dollar forgiveness clause. In essence, they learned that if they had an acceptable credit rating, they could borrow three thousand dollars at very little cost. Many homeowners were obviously seeking loans for purposes other than the earthquake-damage repair they purported to have. The suspicions, in fact, grew so strong that by the end of 1971, Small Business Administration officials were asking borrowers to swear that the money they were receiving would be used for earthquake repairs and were warning them that perjury could net them five years in jail and a substantial fine.

The oaths apparently had little effect. In early 1972, one SBA appraiser in charge of a twelve-man survey team told *The Wall Street Journal* that reports from inspectors indicated that "thousands" of disaster-loan borrowers had used their money in expenditures unrelated to earthquake damage. According to the appraiser, an analysis of twenty-four hundred of the earliest loans showed that by early 1972, repairs to earthquake damages had not been completed in almost 47 percent of the cases. In almost 5 percent of the cases, the analysis showed, the borrowers had not spent a dime of the loan money they had received. According to the *Journal*, when an SBA inspector visited one man in 1972 who had borrowed three thousand dollars to fix his badly battered garage, the garage was still a mess—though the space in front of it was graced by a brand-new seventeen-foot powerboat and a trailer to haul it to and from the ocean.

To add to its troubles, once the SBA dropped its three-estimate requirement, it apparently opened itself to massive fraud. According to a *Los Angeles Times* investigation, janitors, pool builders, carpenters, friends, and neighbors became contractors ready and willing—though not particularly able—to give written estimates to anyone who asked for them. Absurd repair estimates were written on minor earthquake damages. Estimates were written for homeowners who wanted to repair damage not even remotely connected with the earthquake. The problem of unlicensed and fly-by-night estimators became so serious, the *Los Angeles Times* investigators found, that in the city of San Fernando alone, more than five hundred persons were cited for operating without a local contractor's license. One man had two hundred signed contracts for work in his pocket when he was arrested. Many of these contractors padded their estimates to make themselves rich. Others padded them for homeowners who promised them repair work related or not to the quake plus a rebate as a bonus for making an inflated estimate. In many cases, the *Times* charged, homeowners received loans based on faulty estimates, padded and otherwise, but then performed the work themselves, saving themselves the cost of labor and thereby pocketing the difference.

Had the SBA bothered to maintain local staff up to the task of dealing with earthquake devastation, many of the false and misleading estimates might have been avoided. To meet the crush of applications, the SBA rushed staff appraisers from other states into California. These men were not familiar with California construction or material costs and were hardly up to confirming or rejecting the repair estimates submitted by unlicensed and unscrupulous contractors and homeowners. Even less qualified were many of the aerospace engineers temporarily hired to be appraisers. While SBA officials said that these ersatz appraisers had had ample training to do their job, some engineers told the *Times* that they had been given half a day of orientation, followed by only half a day of field training in the company of an experienced man before they were shoved off on their own. At the height of the homeowner rush to obtain SBA funds, the harried appraisers—SBA staffers and aerospace engineers together—were being asked to inspect up to fifteen homes a day, the equivalent of one house every half hour. As a result, appraisers cut only $15 million from the first $191 million requested by Los Angeles homeowners to repair alleged damages. No one has been able to estimate how many millions of dollars SBA's inadequate response to the quake cost the federal government.

To some extent, the February 9 earthquake served to jolt government agencies into new thinking patterns about their disaster-relief procedures. The SBA will certainly be among the first to be overhauled, and by early 1972 SBA officials, Congress, and the Nixon Administration were all fashioning plans to improve the agency's response. One SBA recommendation was that the entire program be turned over to the Department of Housing and Urban Development, whose larger staffs would find it easier to cope with the deluge of work brought on by an earthquake in a heavily urbanized area.

The February 9 earthquake also jolted the Office of Emergency Preparedness (OEP) into developing a more coordinated and effective federal response to earthquake devastation. Coming to grips with the realization that earthquakes of varying magnitudes, depths, sites, and fault origin could have vastly different effects, OEP asked the National Oceanic and Atmospheric Administration (NOAA) and some California agencies to estimate the effects of dissimilar earthquakes on urban areas, including their utilities, roads, hospitals, and local disaster-relief efforts. Once the information is available, OEP hopes other federal agencies will draw up contingency plans to meet a number of probable postearthquake situations.

Whether some of this new-found commitment to earthquake relief work will retain its momentum remains to be seen. The February 9 earthquake gave public officials an all too uncomfortable preview of what they could expect in future shocks striking urbanized California. The quake made it all too obvious that intensive measures to strengthen buildings would have to be undertaken if Californians are to be protected; that special interests eager for land development everywhere will have to be stilled; and that, given the inadequate preparations that have been made to date, entirely new relief and rescue plans and operations will have to be financed. However, such a comprehensive response to the earthquake threat is more than most officials, from the local building inspector to the most senior senator, are willing to face. They are, therefore, eager to ignore substantive approaches to earthquake safety and are easily drawn to two seemingly simpler and promising solutions to earthquake danger: prediction and prevention of tremors.

Chapter Ten

In 1941, during one of his deep trances, the mystic Edward Cayce somberly warned a worried man who had come to him for advice on the future that Los Angeles, San Francisco, and New York would be destroyed in the immediate decades following 1958. Despite the man's entreaties, Cayce refused to say any more. But later, one of his disciples narrowed the focus somewhat, predicting that the apocalypse would come to California at 3:13 P.M. on a Friday. Having said that much, he too withdrew into silence. Which Friday it would be, remained a mystery.

The predictions, like so many put forth by spiritualists, faded into a well-deserved oblivion. But in early January of 1969, the California Institute of Technology Press Office, in one of those press releases that invariably find their way into the wastebaskets of assistant city editors, announced that two of the institution's scientists felt that some degree of creep could probably be expected along the San Andreas Fault in early April.

Although the announcement hardly made news, it somehow fell into the hands of some of California's practicing
psychics. Among them were those who remembered the
predictions by Cayce and his disciple, and they saw in the
press release the much-awaited sign that the end was finally
at hand for California. Now they knew it would be in 1969,
in April, on a Friday. Before long shops selling occult supplies could barely keep up with the demand for paraphernalia
lia the true believers needed to confirm the exact moment of
the cataclysm.

There were those, of course, who could see no reason to
pinpoint an exact date. California was doomed, so why stay
around to worry about the precise date and time? Early in
1969, a twenty-eight-year-old housewife named Elizabeth
Steen, a self-proclaimed seer, simply led her entire family,
and whatever friends she could persuade to come along, in
an exodus from California to Spokane, Washington, to avoid
the April earthquake. Some fundamentalist preachers announced from the pulpits that God himself had visited them
in 1968 and had advised them to get themselves and their
flocks out of California. The Lord, they said, was determined to punish Californians for their evil ways and would
probably do so in 1969. In trailing campers, buses, cars,
some left for the new promised lands suggested by the God
of their visions—Missouri, Tennessee, and Georgia.

(When the February 9 earthquake struck Los Angeles,
the self-exiled announced that the tremor was only a taste of
things to come. "Los Angeles has exalted itself as the City of
the Angels," one preacher who had taken his congregation
of two hundred to Georgia said when he learned of the disaster. "It's going to be brought down to its grave. We believe that [it] is more or less a repetition of what happened
in the time of Christ to Capernaum. Christ prophesied that
Capernaum had exalted itself to the heavens and it would

be brought down to hell. Today, most of it is under the sea.")

Out of the confusion of the various prophecies, one date began to be mentioned with increasing frequency: April 4, Good Friday, the fifth anniversary of the Good Friday earthquake in Anchorage, Alaska. As the appointed time for the catastrophe approached, the crescendo mounted. Explanations by respected geophysicists (including some from Caltech, where there was some embarrassment over the university's inadvertent role in the mania) that even the worst earthquakes had been responsible for earth movements of only twenty feet—and certainly had never been responsible for the annihilation of an area the size of California—were roundly ignored. On the other hand, statements by some seismologists that yes, a good-sized earthquake was always a possibility were seized and distorted with alacrity. A statement by a visiting physicist (who was also an amateur earthquake watcher) from the University of Michigan that he was leaving the state because he could not in good conscience subject his family to the great earthquake that would certainly come *someday* received wide circulation.

The Fellowship of the Ancient Mind, a Druid order claiming to be both telepathic and more than six thousand years old, appeared at Los Angeles City Hall to apply for salvage permits that would allow its members to rescue the state's works of art after the earthquake. Members of the society, the Druids said, would stay behind in any case to study the earthquake as "an art form . . . the greatest example of destructive art in history." And, while a sixty-six-dollar permit fee they could not meet temporarily side-tracked their rescue plans, the Druids did agree to give everyone at least two days warning when they themselves were made privy to the secret of the quake's exact date.

Others were not made so charitable by the shadow of impending doom. A number of San Franciscans publicly hoped for the earthquake because they were convinced that the tremor and its accompanying tidal waves would flood a wide area between San Francisco and Los Angeles, turning southern California into an island that would float off to sea and out of the life of the more cultural and sophisticated north. Since the predicted earthquake, which some said would shake one side of the state into the sea, was to center along the San Andreas Fault, hippies bought picks, shovels, and spades and announced that on the day of the earthquake they would gather at the giant fault to help pry it loose and send at least half of California cascading into the ocean.

Nervous jokes—Howard Hughes was buying Nevada so he could have ocean-front property—began making the rounds. Songs about earthquakes soaked the airwaves.

With all the rumors—duly noted tongue in cheek by radio, television, newspapers, and national magazines in search of light relief from the oppressive fare of daily news —growing in frequency and deepening in gloom, even some sober and rational people began to have the smallest of gnawing doubts. Caltech, the USGS, and the California Division of Mines offices throughout the state were hard pressed to answer the phone calls and letters from anxiety-stricken people. The Los Angeles Civil Defense Office received nearly fifteen hundred calls and hundreds of letters in the weeks preceding Good Friday. Most of the calls were from people who knew their fears were groundless, but wanted to reassure themselves just the same. A few calls and letters, said William Frank, coordinator of the office, were from people who demanded to "know who was behind the plot to suppress information about the earthquake."

A few people even began to keep an eye on the comings and goings of the better-known geophysicists and seismologists in the state. The dean of the earthquake scientists, Dr.

Charles Richter, was forced to issue a public statement denying a rumor that he and his wife planned to leave California for all of April. He and his wife, the professor said, would stay in Pasadena and, along with their cat, take their chances along with everyone else.

"The annual meeting of the Seismological Society of America was held in St. Louis during the first four days of April, and this raised some eyebrows," Dr. Louis C. Pakiser of the USGS said jokingly. Although he skipped that meeting, he did attend others out of the state in April—but not without having to give friends and neighbors a lot of reassuring explanations. Before leaving for one end-of-April meeting, Dr. Pakiser sought to reassure his "followers" that there was no scientific reason to believe that California would disappear under the waves. As proof, he said, he would even leave his wife behind. "This," he said, "did not seem to help matters. I thought I'd better make some special effort to try to reassure these people, so I phoned my mother-in-law in Arizona and asked her if she could come out and stay with the wife. When I told the neighbors that I had done this, all faith in me was lost."

Although scientists joke about the persistent efforts by psychics to deliver themselves of accurate predictions about cataclysmic California earthquakes, many geophysicists and seismologists, not to mention a good number of laymen, would like nothing better than to find some method of anticipating tremors, major and minor.

Some researchers have tried to make some premonitory sense out of phenomena not directly associated with the earthquake mechanisms. They have suggested, for example, that several species of animals might serve as living early warning systems to the approach of earthquakes. They point out that pheasants are often highly disturbed prior to an

earthquake and that even such traditionally lethargic creatures as catfish turn skittish hours before a tremor strikes.
Before massive Chilean earthquakes in 1822 and 1835, it is
said, flocks of sea gulls, frightened by disturbances in the
ocean, flew inland. Dogs in Talcahuano ran howling through
the streets before the 1835 earthquake. Before the 1906
earthquake, dogs howled in San Francisco throughout the
night, and before an earthquake in Taal, in the Philippines,
frightened dogs, cats, and cows sent up such a cacophony of
yelps, howls, and bellows at two in the morning that many
residents of the city ran into the streets, cheating death
when a severe earthquake shattered their homes minutes
later.

At least one scientist, wanting to leave "no stone un-
turned" as he put it, tried to find if a link between earthquakes and astrological phenomena could really be determined. The scientist, a geophysicist named Roger N.
Hunter, studied what astrology students know as conjunc-
tions, squares, and oppositions of planets. He cataloged
eclipses that closely followed each other, the movements of
any planet that crossed any space in the sky where there
had been a recent eclipse of the sun or the moon, and the
movement of one planet across an area where there had
been an eclipse of a second planet. None of these events,
Hunter found, could be correlated to any significant degree
with the occurrence of earthquakes.

While Hunter did remain skeptical that planetary and
stellar movements could be used to predict the times and
locations of earthquakes, he pulled short of stating that absolutely no correlations could exist between the movements
of heavenly bodies and shaking in the earth. In 1959, for example, a professor at the University of Munich demonstrated that during fifteen of twenty-three earthquakes of
magnitude 7 or more, the planet Uranus had been directly
above or below the meridian. The results of the German's

observations were interesting, Hunter said, because the chances that a planet would be in the same position during a number of earthquakes was less than four times out of a hundred. "So, despite the fact that the known physical effects of the planetary positions are far too small to cause or even trigger earthquakes," Hunter speculated, "we cannot rule out absolutely the possibility that there may be some reliable correlations between them which could be used to predict earthquakes. The psychiatrist Carl Jung coined a word for it, 'acausal synchronicity,' the idea that two events may be synchronized, one always following another, with no cause-and-effect relationship between them. A simple example would be two clocks. They keep pace with one another quite reliably, yet neither one has any direct physical effect on the other."

A few geophysicists have been studying natural events— changes in underground gas and water pressures, shifts in the earth's magnetic field—that often accompany earthquakes, hoping the changes might yield clues for predicting seismic activity. In March, 1969, for example, a German geologist noted the presence of abnormally high concentrations of methane gas in a shaft being used to study the geology of a region in southern Germany, after the region had been struck by an earthquake. Crustal movements leading to the quake, the geologist reasoned, may have freed larger quantities of the gas. As long as the high leakage continued, he thought, the forces that had brought about the crust movement were still in effect. Thus, he said, it was quite possible that a second earthquake would soon strike. His prediction proved to be right when a second tremor did hit the area. Thereafter, the methane gas quantities dropped back to normal levels. Soviet geophysicists also have tried to predict earthquakes by tracking increases and decreases in the leakage of radon, a rare radioactive gas, in seismic areas.

Changes in the pressures of underground water and oil wells have also been seen to precede an earthquake. Measurements taken in the oil wells near the epicenter of the 1952 Kern County earthquake showed that casing pressures two to four days after the tremor were as much as ten times above normal. Furthermore, researchers found, two of the earthquake's strongest aftershocks also came when casing pressures were at their highest points. In the two weeks following the earthquake activity, the pressures fell to 20 percent below their normal level and returned to the usual levels only after several months.

A geologist on the Santa Barbara campus of the University of California, A. G. Sylvester, has pointed out that abnormal oil flows could be seen during an earthquake sequence that led to a strong shock in the Santa Barbara area on June 29, 1925. A small foreshock struck the area a few hours before the main earthquake. A few minutes after the foreshock but some time before the main quake, oil began to seep out onto the Santa Barbara beach. Similarly, in December, 1969, and January, 1970, observers found that oil seeps onto the beach increased and decreased just before two minor earthquakes struck in the central part of the Santa Barbara Channel.

At the Boulder Laboratories of NOAA, a senior research fellow, J. S. Rinehart, has proposed the theory that geysers, including Old Faithful in Yellowstone National Park, could serve as natural gauges capable of giving early warnings of earthquakes in areas near the geysers.

Old Faithful's eruptions have been studied, timed, and recorded for at least one hundred years. And although the famous geyser has earned its reputation because its spectacular explosions are fairly predictable, some variations in the intervals between its performances have always been noted. Studying the variations in the pauses between sprays and attempting to link them to earthquakes in a sixty-mile region around Yellowstone, Rinehart found some interesting correlations. Over the years, the average interval between explosions has been sixty-five minutes. But between two and four years before every major earthquake around Yellowstone, the interval suddenly begins to shorten, reaching a minimal time just before an earthquake strikes. After the shock, the time between eruptions begins to lengthen. Before an earthquake on December 20, 1908, Rinehart says, the interval between Old Faithful's spurts dropped from sixty-seven minutes to sixty-five. After the 1908 quake, the time lapses began to lengthen until they reached seventy-seven minutes between explosions in 1919. Over the next few years, the time span between eruptions began to drop sharply until it reached sixty-two minutes, the length noted when a strong earthquake hit the area on June 27, 1925.

It may also be possible, the NOAA scientist says, that Old Faithful may be affected by events that precede distant earthquakes. The 1964 Anchorage earthquake, Rinehart says, was also anticipated by a progressive decrease in the time span between Old Faithful's eruptions.

Just as some have looked to changes in underground pressures in gas, water, and oil supplies for clues to earthquake prediction, others have looked to another part of the earth's environment—its magnetic field—for alterations that could be used as telltale signs of an approaching tremor.

The earth's magnetic field, scientists know, is marked by peculiarities other than its propensity to reverse its orientation every few hundred thousand or million years. Since 1890, geophysicists have known that the earth's north pole describes a kind of wobbly, counterclockwise circle some forty feet in diameter about every fourteen months. When geophysicists compared the dates of twenty-two major earthquakes with the dates in which the pole had shifted abruptly in its circular route, they found correlations between earthquakes and sudden shifts in fifteen of twenty-two instances. More important, they found that the path fluctuations had occurred from one to eighteen days before five of the most severe earthquakes and from eight to fifteen days before three of the seven next most severe earthquakes. Similarly, some preliminary links have been noted between earthquakes and changes in the magnetic field in an area where an earthquake strikes. Just before the 1964 Alaskan earthquake, oil engineers working with a magnetometer near Anchorage noted that their instrument indicated a mysterious and puzzling shift in the area's magnetic field. An hour later, the Good Friday earthquake struck. Other geophysicists have found evidence that magnetometers detect sudden shifts in the magnetic field shortly before an earthquake. These studies have spurred the development and placement of highly sensitive magnetometers scientists hope will provide further clues to the links between the earth's magnetic field and earthquakes.

While changes in oil-well pressures or sudden shifts in the magnetic field before earthquakes fascinate some earth scientists, others are convinced that these episodes are essentially irrelevant to earthquake prediction and could, even if refined, amount to no more than a sophisticated crystal-ball approach. Those who want to anticipate earthquakes, some scientists say, should spend their time studying the mechanisms directly associated with earth movements.

Yet even the scientists oriented to direct observation of the earthquake mechanisms are divided. Some geophysicists think that earthquake prediction will come only after they have learned more about the behavior of rocks under stress. These geophysicists have reported that their laboratory work already has yielded clues that could someday be used to predict earthquakes. When tremendous forces are applied to rocks, under laboratory conditions, the researchers say, the volume of the rocks begins to expand when that pressure reaches 90 percent of the total pressure needed to fracture the rock samples. Monitoring of rocks around fault areas, they suggest, could detect similar increases in volume and warn that the rocks were nearing the breaking point. Other investigators have reported that rocks subjected to pressure in laboratory experiments show an increase in what researchers call microseismic activity—infinitesimally small shudders in the rocks. The occurrence of these "quakelings" in the laboratory rocks, they say, suggests that the rocks were already cracking on a small scale before the final break. These prebreak changes could also be taking place in the larger rocks surrounding real faults, the investigators say. They hope that given enough sensitive instrumentation along major faults, similar changes could be monitored in rocks surrounding faults.

Others argue that the changes detected in a laboratory could be radically different in the "real" world. In a natural setting, the doubters say, the temperatures and physical characteristics of the rocks would affect the preearthquake changes in some mysterious and perhaps even unfathomable way. Furthermore, they argue, even if all the different ways various rocks react to pressures or varying temperatures could be measured, even if some vital processes that immediately precede a major break in one part of the fault could be discerned, circumstances and conditions can vary so much from one section of a fault to another and from one fault to the next that separate and viable prediction machinery and methods would have to be worked out for an unmanageable number of situations.

Geophysicists and seismologists who question the approach to earthquake prediction through the study of actions and reactions within rocks suggest that it might be wiser to concentrate on some of the broader activity preceding tremors. Movements along a fault, total accumulation of strain, patterns in the incidence of small earthquakes, and tilts along wide sections of crust, they suggest, might give better clues to earthquake prediction. The manner in which streams have been offset by the San Andreas, for example, could be a clue to successful earthquake prediction. "We will eventually see how the earth's crust has been offset progressively by a few feet to perhaps a hundred miles during the recent geologic past," Lou Pakiser of the USGS says. "This will give us a better idea for predicting the pattern of earthquakes and other fault movements. From such studies we eventually expect to predict the rate of earthquakes and have a better idea of just when they will occur."

Some geophysicists suggest that if a fault is characterized by creep action, changes in the crawl rate might be warnings that an earthquake is on its way. Survey crews for the California state agencies have found, for example, that survey lines across a fault contract as time progresses, an indication that strain is being wound into the fault. When surveying data are studied after earthquakes, the data have usually shown that some months before an earthquake strikes, the rate at which the survey lines contract quickens at an appreciable rate. Then suddenly the contraction stops and the survey lines begin to lengthen. Some time after the lengthening phase has set in, there is an earthquake. Although a great deal of work remains to be done, some geophysicists believe that refined interpretations of the survey-line contraction-expansion process, correlated with accurate measurements of accumulating strain along a fault, could lead to earthquake forecasts.

In their research into eighteenth-, nineteenth-, and twentieth-century earthquakes, Japanese scientists have discovered what they feel may be a reliable clue to earthquake prediction. Distinct changes in the altitude and inclination of land, they say, could be correlated with previous earthquakes.

Records from an earthquake in Ajigasawa in 1793 showed that the region along the Sea of Japan rose more than three feet almost four hours before an earthquake hit the region. An 1802 earthquake in Sado, records showed, was preceded by a land rise of more than seven feet half an hour before the earthquake. A Hamada earthquake in 1872 was anticipated by a six-and-a-half-foot rise half an hour before the shaking began, and the Tango earthquake in 1927 was foreshadowed by a four-foot rise in the nearby region two and a half hours before the disaster. Almost nine years before the Niigata earthquake, bench markers in the area just north of the quake's epicenter began to detect a rise in the area almost five times as great as the rise of preceding years. The precipitous rise continued until 1959, when the rate of ascent began to diminish. Eventually, the rise stopped altogether and the land began to fall, a motion it continued almost until the quake struck in 1964.

The Japanese discovery that regions move where an earthquake will strike found partial confirmation in studies of some American seismic activity. In 1970, two Stanford graduates, working toward Ph.D.'s in different fields, "discovered" that two earthquakes in the San Francisco Bay Area had been preceded by tilts in the ground.

The two students, Darroll Wood and Stephen R. Levine, stumbled upon their findings by chance. Levine, a computer specialist, looking for raw scientific data a computer could be made to "translate" into a graph that could be animated on a televisionlike screen, offhandedly told Wood, a neighborhood friend, about his needs. Wood, a candidate for a Ph.D. in geophysics at Stanford, mentioned that the USGS National Center for Earthquake Research, in Menlo Park, had raw computer-recorded data from several stations where instruments were measuring tilts in the land around Berkeley and the nearby area, the Presidio. Data were also available from almost one hundred seismometers that had been scattered near various faults along an area stretching from Santa Rosa, north of San Francisco, to San Juan Bautista, south of the Bay Area.

Using the data gathered by these various instruments for a period of ten days before two magnitude 4 earthquakes in the Bay Area, Levine punched out a computer program that would analyze all the data collected by the instrument network. That computer immediately showed that microquakes (too small to be felt by people) and very slight tremors increased steadily as the hour of the first strong shock approached. Thus, the computer demonstrated that intense monitoring efforts of faults might detect the onset of miniquake activity and warn of an oncoming major tremor.

The big bonus in Levine and Wood's work rested in the computer's work with the tilt data. The computer clearly showed that twenty-nine hours before the first big earthquake, the beginnings of a slight tilt could be detected—a tilt that increased steadily during the next nineteen hours. Furthermore, the computer showed, the tilt was not just in any direction, but toward the area where the epicenter of the first quake would be. In other words, just before the earthquake, the Bay Area had tilted toward the epicenter of the quake. When the strain had been relieved, the area tilted back to its normal alignment.

Many of the instruments and techniques available to seismologists and geophysicists have been highly refined in the last few years. To the sorrow of scientists interested in prediction, however, there are too few of the instruments available. Thus, all the data that would be used as indices that might be useful in forecasting earthquakes—the lengthening and shortening of survey lines, the measurements of accumulating strain, the observations of land tilt—are, for the moment, not available in the quantities needed to support adequate prediction attempts. Countless observations and measurements, checks and double checks of every individual clue will have to be made for a variety of situations before that particular indicator finds acceptance in any prediction lexicon. For example, if survey lines contract and expand prior to earthquakes, what combinations of contraction and expansion presage a 4.5 earthquake? A 6.6 quake? An 8.3 tremor? Furthermore, even as each clue is refined and extensively defined, it will have to be dovetailed with many other indicators. What, seismologists would have to ask themselves, would a contraction of .35 centimeters and an expansion of .55 centimeters in a survey line mean when combined with a half-foot rise and tilt in the Bay Area region? And how would variations in these factors along two or more faults lying close to each other in the same area— the San Andreas and the Hayward for example—affect potential prediction formulas?

Anticipating the complexities of arriving at accurate prediction processes, a very small group of researchers has proposed that prediction could be completely bypassed. More attention, they think, should be paid to the prevention of earthquakes.

The seeds for this seemingly far-fetched idea were planted by accident. Toward the end of the 1950s, munition makers and designers at the United States Rocky Mountain Arsenal near Denver found themselves deluged with fluid wastes accumulating from manufacturing processes at the site. Eager to dispose of the wastes, the Army drilled a well two miles deep in the area, and between March 8, 1962, and February 20, 1966, pumped millions of liters of fluids— sometimes as much as twenty million liters a month—into the giant cesspool.

Almost as soon as the Army's disposal program began, seismograph stations in Colorado began to record flurries of small earthquakes in the Denver area. Seismograph records, furthermore, showed that the earthquakes were hitting within five miles of the Army's new well. By 1966, as earthquakes repeatedly buffeted Denver—sometimes more than seventy would strike in one month—many scientists were convinced that the pumping operations had something to do with the tremors. "The occurrence of a natural earthquake swarm so closely related to the disposal well would be an extremely unlikely coincidence," an investigating team wrote in *Science*. "We consider it highly probable that the release of the stored tectonic strain was triggered by the injection of fluid into the basement rock." In other words, while strain had been accumulating naturally in the earthquake-prone region, it had not yet reached the point where it alone could overcome restraints on the faults. The fluid injected into areas near the faults, however, was literally greasing local rocks, helping the faults overcome the restraints. As ground moved with new ease, earthquakes, quite naturally, struck the area.

The events at the Rocky Mountain Arsenal fitted in nicely with some other scattered but heretofore ignored observations: some seismographs, deployed in or around oil fields where engineers had pumped water into wells to force oil nearer to the pumps, were also recording small shocks in zones where water pressure was the greatest. USGS scientists, who were observing the seismographs, then persuaded the operators of the oil field to reduce the water pressure near the area where the earthquakes had struck. Within a month, the earthquake activity had fallen off drastically—to one or two shocks a month, compared to ten to twenty tremors a month when the water pressure had been kept high. Inevitably the question arose: if fluids, including water, pumped into areas marked by faults, had lubricated the faults accidentally, inducing them to move, why not inject fluids under controlled conditions to goad a fault into action? Theoretically, a fault could be made to move when just enough strain had accumulated to produce a small earthquake, thereby preventing continued accumulation of strain that could eventually result in one massive and destructive tremor. "It is desirable to replace large, rapidly occurring movements over large portions of a fault which result in dangerous earthquakes," says Dr. Charles Archambeau, a Caltech professor of geophysics researching the effects of fluids on faults, "by either a small series of small movements over smaller portions of the fault, or by very slow 'creeping' movements over parts or all of the fault. The injection of water at depths along a fault may do one or both of these things." Dr. Archambeau, along with others hoping to test these theories, has begun small-scale tests on faults in remote regions. If the tests prove successful, the technique could be used, Dr. Archambeau thinks, to prevent great quakes originating in California's faults, including the San Andreas. "The harmful earthquakes in California are those of relatively shallow origin," Dr. Archambeau says. "Even so, we would require deep wells in order to inject water at the appropriate depth. We think that while this might be costly, it is likely to be successful and could very well save not only money but lives."

Those who favor the development of an earthquake-prediction program argue that the benefits would be almost limitless. Given information that an earthquake was in the offing, prediction proponents say, public officials could begin to evacuate persons living in dangerous buildings and to limit access to office and other commercial buildings of doubtful integrity. Presuming that responsible officials have —by the time a prediction program is perfected—devised adequate disaster-relief programs, fire-fighting resources would be deployed to those areas most likely to suffer outbreaks of flames—oil and gas fields, plants using volatile materials, areas of cities crowded with older, wooden buildings.

With the announcement of an impending earthquake, areas near the sea—Venice, Santa Monica, Long Beach, Santa Barbara, the low-lying areas of San Francisco—could be evacuated. Nuclear-power plants would be alerted or even shut down completely if they were within the danger area. Power and gas companies would be asked to seal off vulnerable pipelines lying across the suspected fault or in other areas where they would be subject to excessive tension. Water in reservoirs—like the Van Norman lakes— would be lowered well in advance of the first vibrations. Safe schools and public buildings where evacuees and others affected by the earthquake would find refuge would be well stocked with food, clothing, and bedding. Hospitals could shift to an emergency status, scheduling additional nurses and doctors, and stockpiling machines and emergency equipment.

Prediction enthusiasts also argue that a proper program would, in the long run, save money as well as lives. If all of the state's unsafe structures were to be razed, argues Dr. C. B. Raleigh of the USGS, the cost to the owners and to the public would be immense. "Let's take the example of Los Angeles," he says, "where Professor Duke predicted that 40,000 buildings will collapse in a great earthquake. Duke gave no cost estimate for their replacement but a figure of $100,000 per building is probably conservative. Thus, replacement cost for razing these structures, as suggested by some engineers, is $4 billion." If a prediction program were to be developed, Dr. Raleigh argues, people could be kept away from the buildings in dangerous times and allowed to use them when safe. "The average lifetime of these older buildings in the absence of an earthquake might still be about twenty-five years. So, for each year that goes by before they are razed, the savings allowed by a prediction program would be $160 million. In fact, the savings realized from only six months additional lifetime before razing of California's hazardous buildings, if razing is ultimately adopted, would pay for the entire prediction program."

Talk of prediction and prevention, as desirable as they might seem, sets a good number of teeth to gnashing around California. Preventing an 8.3 earthquake, for example, by purposefully triggering a series of tremors measuring 4 or 5 on the Richter scale may seem to be a good idea—until it is recognized that a "small" 4.9 or 5.5 earthquake could in itself cause severe damage if, escaping control, it were to hit too near a large city or town. "I hope someone researches the financial liabilities of causing even small earthquakes," Henry Degenkolb says. "Who pays for the broken expensive art object that falls to the floor in a small earthquake caused by some enterprising research worker? I also hope that before we cause small earthquakes here, we learn how they relate to the world's structure along the earthquake belts. Can you imagine the international incident if we knowingly prevented a major earthquake from happening here but in the process caused other stresses to be relieved in Chile, Japan or Vladivostok in the U.S.S.R.?"

Many experts, especially engineers, object strenuously to the sudden fascination with earthquake prediction. Even if breakthroughs are made in earthquake prediction, some experts say, by 1982 or 1983, forecasters will be able to do no more than say that, according to all indications, an earthquake will strike "in the next few weeks or months." The ideal twenty-four-hour warning system, says Dr. Clarence Allen, "is for the moment completely unrealistic."

For many years to come, says Henry Degenkolb, who is no more enchanted with earthquake prediction than he is with earthquake prevention, "it is probable that we could not predict the timing of earthquakes to any greater degree of precision than we can predict the weather. We have studied the weather for centuries, we spend a considerable amount of money on our weather bureau and we even have satellites studying the cloud patterns. All this for good reason—for much of our economy is concerned with the weather. And yet, with all our money and effort we express our prediction in percentage chances—fortunately for the meteorologists for they are frequently wrong."

Even if a warning could be given to expect a 70 percent chance of an earthquake in a period of two weeks after the prediction is published, the effects on a city, region, or state would be questionable. Thousands of persons might be encouraged to leave their unsafe homes or apartment buildings as a result of the prediction. Would enough alternative housing be available? How long would they stay there? Who would pay for their alternate quarters? Would the warnings also apply to people who live or work in new, but marginally built structures? Would they too have to leave their homes and places of residence? Would they too stop going to work? Finally, how would the population bear the uncertainty of living with an earthquake forecast that would stretch over any period longer than twenty-four hours? "Can you imagine," asks Degenkolb, "the effect on the economy of San Francisco or Los Angeles if an authoritative and informed prediction were to be made that there was a 60 percent chance of a major earthquake in the next six months? Can you imagine the economic loss that would occur if it did not happen in six or even eighteen months?"

Perhaps those who favor earthquake forecasts are right; perhaps a reliable earthquake-prediction mechanism is the best hope for dealing with California's seismic problems, and perhaps, as Frank Press, a geophysicist, says, obstructing earthquake-forecasting research on panic or economic-loss grounds is "shortsighted." Yet, even the most optimistic of the forecast advocates admit that a minimal prediction capability would cost almost one hundred million to develop and would take a minimum of ten years to refine. Thus, the suspicion lingers that both the money and the time might be better spent.

Despite advances made over the last quarter of a century, earthquake experts know too little about the effects of earthquake forces on buildings and soils. Some soils engineers and structural engineers may know more than others, but ultimately even the wisest technicians are reduced to guesswork. If money is to be spent on solving earthquake problems, it would be better spent to expand the network of instruments that will accurately gauge the nature of earthquake forces and their effects on soil and on the works of man. If money can be made available for the mitigation of earthquake damage, it would be best used to help cities and towns to hire the men and women capable of closely supervising the development of land and the construction of buildings. A well-planned disbursement of funds will be more effective if it encourages—in the form of tax relief or direct grants—the retirement of hazardous land and the razing of dangerous buildings. "The priority," says Lloyd Cluff, "should not be in the direction of predicting in terms of hours or days of a major earthquake. We already know that we are in a high-seismic-risk zone in California. We know that we have a San Fernando–type earthquake about every two or three years. We know that we are going to have more of these earthquakes and approximately where. The bulk of that money should be spent on geological and engineering studies that will minimize the effects. We know we are going to have more earthquakes, so why attempt to predict exactly when? Let's be better prepared for them when they come."

Bibliography

Anderson, Don L. "The San Andreas Fault." *Scientific American* 225:52 (November, 1971).

Bates, F. L., et al. *Social and Psychological Consequences of a Natural Disaster.* National Academy of Sciences—National Research Council. Disaster Research Group. Disaster Study No. 18.

Brown, Robert D., et al. *The Parkfield-Cholame California Earthquakes of June–August 1966.* Geological Survey Professional Paper 579. Washington, D.C., U.S. Government Printing Office, 1967.

Byerly, Perry. *Seismology.* Englewood Cliffs, New Jersey, Prentice-Hall, Inc., 1942.

California Department of Water Resources. *Alaska Earthquake.* Bulletin 116-5 (October, 1965).

California Division of Mines and Geology. *California Geology* (formerly *Mineral Information Service*). Vol. 24, nos. 4 and 5 (April/May, 1971).

California Division of Mines and Geology. *Mineral Information Service.* Vol. 22, no. 5 (May, 1969).

California Division of Mines and Geology. *Mineral Information Service.* Vol. 23, no. 3 (March, 1970).

California Division of Mines and Geology. *Mineral Information Service.* Vol. 23, no. 7 (July, 1970).

California Resources Agency. Proceedings of the Earthquake and Geologic Hazards Conference, San Francisco, December 7 and 8, 1964.

California State Department of Education. *A Report on Structurally Unsafe School Buildings.* Sacramento, January, 1971.

California State Department of Education. *A Report to the State Board of Education.* Los Angeles, December 9, 1971.

California State Department of Education. *Cracks in the Belfry.* Sacramento, 1969.

California State Legislature. *Preliminary Report on the San Fernando Earthquake.* Joint Committee on Seismic Safety, July 31, 1971.

California State Legislature. *Transcript of Hearing on Highway Structural Safety.* Subcommittee on Highway Structural Safety, June 8, 1971.

Clark, William B., and Hauge, Carl J. "When the Earth Quakes, You Can Reduce the Danger." *California Geology.* Vol. 24, no. 11 (November, 1971).

"Codes Slow to Adapt to Quake Data." *Engin. News* 74:43 (February 11, 1965).

Crawshaw, Ralph. "Reactions to a Disaster." *Archives of Gen. Psych.* 9:157 (August, 1963).

Dalrymple, G. Brent, and Lanphere, Marvin A. *Potential Earthquake Hazards on Bay Fill and Marshland Adjacent to San Francisco Bay.* Testimony to the San Francisco Bay Conservation and Development Commission, December, 1964.

Degenkolb, Henry J. "Earthquake Engineering." Lecture Notes.

Dickinson, William R., and Grantz, Arthur. *Proceedings of a Con-*

ference on Geologic Problems of the San Andreas Fault System. Stanford University Publications, Vol. 11 (1968).

Duke, C. Martin. *Earthquakes and Life Lines.* Paper presented to the Structural Engineers Association of California, October 8, 1971.

Eiby, G. A. *About Earthquakes.* New York, Harper & Row, 1957.

Eiby, G. A. *Earthquakes.* London, Frederick Muller, Ltd., 1957.

Executive Office of the President. *Earthquake Hazard Reduction.* Washington, D.C., U.S. Government Printing Office, August, 1970.

Executive Office of the President. *Q-Day + 100: The Federal Response to the California Earthquake of February 9, 1971.* Washington, D.C., 1971.

Farber, Irving J. "Psychological Aspects of Mass Disaster." *J. Nat. Med. Ass.* 59:340 (September, 1967).

Fritz, Charles E., and Mathewson, J. H. *Convergence Behavior in Disasters: A Problem in Social Control.* Washington, D.C., National Research Council, 1957.

Gutenberg, Beno, and Richter, Charles F. *Seismicity of the Earth.* New York, Hafner Publishing Co., Inc., 1954.

Heck, Nicholas Hunter. *Earthquakes.* New York, Hafner Publishing Co., Inc., 1936.

Hobbs, William Herbert. *Earthquakes, An Introduction to Seismic Geology.* London, Sidney-Appleton, 1908.

Hodgson, John H. *Earthquakes and Earth Structure.* Englewood Cliffs, New Jersey, Prentice-Hall, Inc., 1964.

Hospital Forum. *Disasters and Hospitals.* Vol. 14, no. 10 (January, 1972).

Human Organization. *Human Adaptation to Disaster.* Vol. 16, no. 2 (Summer, 1957).

Hunter, Roger N. "Is There a Connection Between Astrology and Earthquakes?" *Earthquake Information Bulletin.* Vol. 3, no. 3 (May/June, 1971).

Iacopi, Robert. *Earthquake Country.* Menlo Park, California, Lane Books, 1964.

Institute of Governmental Studies. *In the Interest of Earthquake Safety.* Berkeley, University of California, 1971.

Isacks, Bryan, Oliver, Jack, and Sykes, Lynn R. "Seismology and the New Global Tectonics." *J. Geophys. R.* 73:5855 (September 15, 1968).

Jacoby, Wolfgang R. "Instability in the Upper Mantle and Global Plate Movements." *J. Geophys. R.* 75:5671 (October 10, 1970).

James, William. *Memories and Studies.* New York, Longmans, Green and Company, 1911.

Jeffreys, Harold. *Earthquakes and Mountains.* London, Methuen and Co., Ltd., 1935.

Killian, Lewis M. "The Significance of Multigroup Membership in a Disaster." *Am Journal Sociology* 57:309 (January, 1952).

Kuesel, Thomas. "Bay Area Transit System Designed to Roll with Earthquake." *Engin. News.* 176:24 (April 21, 1966).

Lachman, R., and Bonk, W. J. "Behavior and Beliefs During the Recent Volcanic Eruption at Kapoho, Hawaii." *Science* 131:1095 (April 15, 1960).

Langdon, Ray J., and Parker, Allen H. "Psychiatric Aspects of the March 27, 1964, Earthquake." *Alaska Medicine* 6:32 (June, 1964).

Larkin, D. G. "Readiness for an Earthquake." *Am. Wat. Works Ass. J.* 61:405 (August, 1969).

Lee and Praszker, Seed, H. Bolton, and Steinbrugge, Karl V. *Fill: Three Reports on Aspects of Fill in San Francisco Bay.* San Francisco Bay Conservation and Development Commission, May, 1967.

Leet, Don L. *Causes of Catastrophes.* New York, McGraw-Hill Book Co., 1948.

Leet, Don L., and Leet, Florence. *Earthquake.* New York, Dell Publishing Co., Inc., 1971.

Le Pichon, Xavier. "Sea Floor Spreading and Continental Drift." *J. Geophys. R.* 73:3661 (June 15, 1968).

Light, Herman C. "Which Buildings Fail?" *Am. Inst. Arch. J.* 42:37 (December, 1964).

Los Angeles County Earthquake Commission. *San Fernando Earthquake, February 9, 1971* (report). November, 1971.

Macelwane, James B. (SJ). *When the Earth Quakes.* New York, The Bruce Publishing Company, 1947.

Moore, Harry Estill. "Some Emotional Concomitants of Disaster." *Mental Hygiene* 42:45 (January, 1958).

Morgan, W. Jason. "Rises, Trenches, Great Faults and Crustal Blocks." *J. Geophys. R.* 73:1959 (March, 15, 1968).

Nason, Robert D., and Tocher, Don. "Measurement of Movement on the San Andreas Fault," *Earthquake Displacement Fields and the Rotation of the Earth.* Dordrecht, Holland, D. Reidel Publishing Co., 1970.

National Academy of Sciences. *The San Fernando Earthquake of February 9, 1971: Lessons from a Moderate Earthquake on the Fringe of a Densely Populated Region.* Washington, D.C., 1971.

Oakeshott, Gordon B. "San Andreas Fault: Geologic and Earthquake History." *Mineral Information Service* 19:159 (October, 1966).

Office of Emergency Planning. *Report of Earthquake Seminar,* Santa Rosa, California, June 13–14, 1967.

Office of Emergency Preparedness. Proceedings of Geologic Hazards and Public Problems Conference, May 27–28, 1969.

Page, Robert. "Focal Depth of Aftershocks." *J. Geophys. R.* 73:3897 (June 15, 1968).

Pakiser, Louis C., et al. "Earthquake Prediction and Control." *Science* 66:1467 (December 19, 1969).

Phinney, Robert A. *The History of the Earth's Crust. A Symposium.* Princeton, Princeton University Press, 1960.

Popovic, M. and Petrovic, D. "After the Earthquake." *Lancet* 11:1169 (November 28, 1964).

Portland Cement Association. *Behavior of Reinforced Concrete*

Structures in the Caracas, Venezuela, Earthquake of July 29, 1967. Portland, Oregon, 1967.

Press, Frank. "A Strategy for an Earthquake Prediction Research Program." *Tectonophysics* 6:11 (July, 1968).

Press, Frank, and Brace, W. F. "Earthquake Prediction." *Science* 152:1575 (June 17, 1966).

Public Works. *California Water Project and Earthquake Engineering* 99:65 (November, 1968).

Quarantelli, Enrico L. "Images of Withdrawal Behavior in Disaster: Some Basic Misconceptions." *Social Probl.* 8:68 (Summer, 1960).

Richter, Charles F. *Elementary Seismology.* San Francisco, W. H. Freeman and Company, 1958.

Richter, Charles F. "Our Earthquake Risk—Facts and Non-Facts." *California Institute of Technology Quarterly,* January, 1964.

Richter, Charles F. "Seismic Regionalization." *Bull. Seis. Soc. Am.* 49:123 (April, 1959).

Rosenman, Stanley. "The Paradox of Guilt in Disaster Populations." *Psychiatric Quarterly Supp.* 30:181 (Part 2, 1956).

San Francisco Bay Conservation and Development Commission. *The Safety of Fills.* September, 1968.

Scott, Stanley. "Preparing for Future Earthquakes: Unfinished Business in the San Francisco Bay Area." *Bulletin of the Institute of Governmental Studies.* Vol. 9, no. 6. Berkeley, University of California, December, 1968.

Seed, H. Bolton. "Landslides During Earthquake Due to Soil Liquefaction." *Am. Soc. C. E. Proc.* 94 (SM 5 No. 6110): 1055 (September, 1968). Correction 95:1123 (July, 1969).

Seed, H. Bolton. "Method for Earthquake Resistant Design of Earth Dams." *Am. Soc. C. E. Proc.* 92 (SM 1 No. 4616): 13 (January, 1966).

Seed, H. Bolton, and Idriss, Izzat M. *Influence of Local Soil Conditions on Building Damage Potential During Earthquakes.*

Earthquake Engineering Research Center. Berkeley, University of California, December, 1969.

Seed, H. Bolton, Idriss I. M., and Dezfulian, H. *Relationships Between Soil Conditions and Building Damage in the Caracas Earthquake of July 29, 1967.* Earthquake Engineering Research Center. Berkeley, University of California, February, 1970.

Scholz, C. II., and Fitch, Thomas J. "Strain Accumulation Along the San Andreas Fault." *J. Geophys. R.* 74:6649 (December 15, 1969).

"The Shake of Things to Come." *Mosaic* 2:10 (Spring, 1971).

Silber, Earle, Perry, Stewart E., and Bloch, Donald. "Patterns of Parent-Child Interaction in a Disaster." *Psychiatry* 21:159 (May, 1958).

Steinbrugge, Karl V. *Earthquake Hazard in the San Francisco Bay Area: A Continuing Problem in Public Policy.* Institute of Governmental Studies. Berkeley, University of California, 1968.

Steinbrugge, Karl V., Cloud, William K., and Scott, Nina H. *The Santa Rosa, California Earthquakes of October 1, 1969.* U.S. Department of Commerce, 1970.

Steinbrugge, Karl V., and Cluff, Lloyd S. "The Caracas, Venezuela, Earthquake of July 29, 1967." *Mineral Information Service.* Vol. 21, no. 1 (January, 1968).

Steinbrugge, Karl V., and Moran, D. F. "An Engineering Study of the Southern California Earthquake of July 21, 1952, and Its Aftershocks." *Bull. Seis. Soc. Am.* 44:201.

Sykes, Lynn R. "Mechanism of Earthquakes and Nature of Faulting on the Mid-Oceanic Ridges." *J. Geophys. R.* 72:213 (April 15, 1967).

Sylvester, A. G. "Fluid Pressure Variations and Prediction of Shallow Earthquakes." *Science* 169:1231 (September 18, 1970).

U.S. Department of Commerce. *Earthquakes.* Washington, D.C., U.S. Government Printing Office, 1969.

U.S. Department of the Interior—Geological Survey. *Possible Earthquake Hazards at the Site of Proposed Foster City.* A Report to FHA, October, 1961.

U.S. Department of the Interior—Geological Survey. *Tectonic Creep in the Hayward Fault Zone.* Washington, D.C., United States Geological Survey, 1966.

U.S. Department of the Interior—Geological Survey and U.S. Department of Commerce—National Oceanic and Atmospheric Administration. *The San Fernando, California, Earthquake of February 9, 1971.* Geological Survey Professional Paper 733. Washington, D. C., U.S. Government Printing Office, 1971.

U.S. House of Representatives. *Federal Involvement in Construction in Hazardous Geologic Areas.* Seventh Report by Committee on Government Operations. House Report 91-429.

U.S. Senate. *Governmental Response to the California Earthquake Disaster of February 1971.* Committee on Public Works Hearings, June 10, 11, and 12, 1971. U.S. Document 92-H22. Washington, D.C., U.S. Government Printing Office, 1971.

Vine, F. J. "Spreading of Ocean Floor: New Evidence." *Science* 154:140 (December 16, 1966).

Wiegel, Robert L. *Earthquake Engineering.* Englewood Cliffs, New Jersey, Prentice-Hall, Inc., 1970.

Wilson, J. Tuzo. "Transform Faults, Oceanic Ridges and Magnetic Anomalies." *Science* 150:483 (October 22, 1965).

Wilson, Rodman, and Rader, William. "Interstate Travel and School Enrollment after Alaska Good Friday Earthquake." *Alaska Medicine* 10:48 (March, 1968).

Yutzy, Daniel. *Community Priorities in the Anchorage Alaska Earthquake, 1964.* Disaster Research Center. Ohio State University, August, 1969.

Index